The Violin

Emile Leipp

University of Toronto Press

VIOLIN

History,
Aesthetics, Manufacture,
and Acoustics

228321

English translation
© *University of Toronto Press 1969*
Printed in Canada
SBN *8020 1608 1*
The original edition of The Violin *was*
published in France in 1965 under the title
Le Violon *by* HERMANN *scientific publications*
Translated by Hildegarde W. Parry

The violin, with its own special shape and dimensions, has been in existence for four centuries. No musical instrument has given rise to such a flood of literary, technical, and scientific publications; and if the present generation hardly plays it at all, it is because its study demands long and persevering effort. Nevertheless, the violin remains the king of the orchestra, and artists of remarkable talent still draw fresh melody from it.

Industrialization invaded the making of stringed instruments long ago, but many craftsmen still make violins for the love of it, haunted by the ideal perfection which Stradivari would have attained.

A certain romanticism has grown up around the instrument, which has been very prejudicial to its attaining perfection. In any case, it is and remains, above all, an instrument to produce sounds, the functioning and acoustic results of which can be objectively defined and explained thanks to the apparatus and methods of investigation which science has now placed at our disposal. But if its functional role is esteemed to be primordial, it is also true that before dwelling on this, it is better to know the instrument thoroughly. With this end in view, I have set forth in this book numerous results of my personal research into the history of the violin, the aesthetics of its form, and the technique of its fabrication. I have played this instrument for many years; I have personally constructed a considerable number of violins which I have covered with varnish of my own composition and mounted with strings prepared by myself; my researches into acoustics have also formed the subject of a thesis at the Sorbonne. The question of the violin is not exhausted, however, and I merely hope to contribute towards a better perception of the numerous problems raised by this endearing instrument.

I would like to thank here those whose material or moral assistance has aided the publication of this work. These are F. X. Carchereux, Master Craftsman, who initiated me many years ago into the art of instrument making; Charles Maillot of Lyons who pioneered the study of harmonic strings summarized in this book; A. Moles who, by his help and advice, enabled me to complete my thesis on musical instruments.

I am especially indebted to Professor Siestrunck, director of the laboratory of physical mechanics of the Faculty of Sciences, thanks to whom the acoustics laboratory, in which we are developing research concerning musical instruments and the perception of musical sounds, has been set up.

Finally I wish to express my gratitude to the members of the commission for literary studies of the C.N.R.S., to Norbert Dufourq, and to Pierre Berès, director of Hermann Publishing House; without their aid this book would probably never have seen the light of day. E. L.

Contents

The violin, the result of a long empirical evolution, can be considered the most perfect of bowed instruments. Universally known and used, its origin is still obscure. Many authors have sought to establish its descent from primitive bowed instruments: Grillet, Vidal, Fétis, in France; Lutgendorf, Ruhlmann, Curt Sachs, in Germany; Hart, Hill, in England; Muchi, Foffa, Peluzzi, in Italy; and many others.

Their works, however, concern bowed instruments in general. It will be well, therefore, to study the direct ancestors of the violin, leaving aside instruments which belong to other groups of the same family. We must first make quite clear what are the morphological and functional peculiarities of the violin. These can be summarized thus:

1 The violin is a stringed instrument played with a bow of horsehair. It is a melodic instrument, essentially easy to handle.
2 The strings are tuned in successive fifths.
3 The fingerboard of the instrument is smooth and has no frets limiting the tones.
4 Its origin is plebeian: only fiddlers of the humbler sort used it to make the populace dance.

The direct ancestors of the violin, therefore, must have all these distinctive characteristics throughout their evolution, and from the primitive type.

Observations on the sound produced by the bowstring and its amplification by a resonant box are certainly as old as the world. The invention of the actual bow, on the contrary, seems to be relatively recent. During the last century a controversy arose between partisans of the oriental system and partisans of the Scandinavian system. The former claim India as the cradle of the first bowed instrument, of which the prototype is said to be the *ravanastron*.

This two-stringed instrument consisted of a small cylinder of hollow wood. A piece of snake-skin was stretched over one of the openings, and upon it rested a bridge bearing the two strings tuned a fifth apart and played with a horse-hair bow. The origin of this instrument is legendary; its invention is attributed to Ravanon, king of Ceylon, who lived five thousand years ago. The descendants of the *ravanastron* appeared in Europe during the Crusades, coming from India by way of Persia and Arabia.

The partisans of the Scandinavian system hold that the bowed instrument existed in Europe well before the Crusades. Its prototype is said to be the *crouth trithant*, the name of which is found in a poem by Venantius Fortunatus, bishop of Poitiers, during the sixth century (33). A picture of this instrument is found in a manuscript of the eleventh century (Abbey of St. Martial, Limoges). This *crouth* has three strings. It has a smooth fingerboard, and it gradually developed into the *crwth* of the Welsh bards, which was still in use towards the end of the eighteenth century. This last instrument had six strings: two low strings (drones) which were plucked with the thumb of the left hand, while the four other strings were played with the bow. The bridge was curved, although the contrary has been asserted; therefore the strings were not co-planar, and consequently were not all played at once. Fétis (33) has given the tuning of this instrument:

drones : G2 and G3;   ⎱ (In the system of pitch notation used here, C1 has a
strings : C4; C3; D3; D4. ⎰ frequency of 65.4 Hz; middle C is C3.)

The drones, therefore, presented a tuning of fifths and of octaves with the open melodic strings.

The Welsh *crwth* was still the same in 1784, if one accepts a document of that period. But there is no proof that the Welsh *crwth* was always played with a bow. It can also be taken as a Greek cithara to which was added a median up-

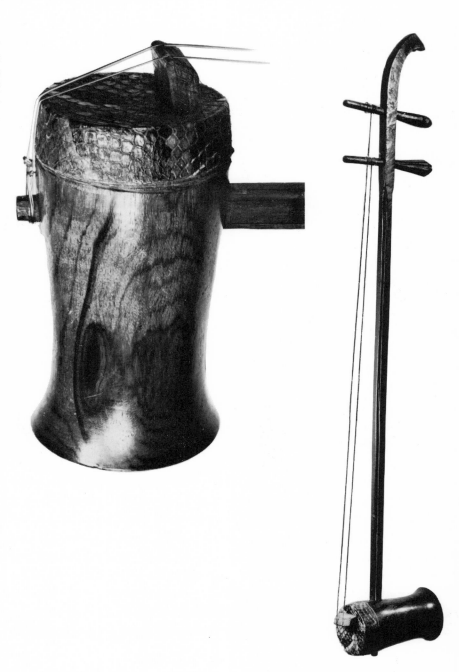

The ravanastron *consists of a cylindrical box covered with snake-skin, traversed by a neck bearing two pegs to which are attached two strings tuned a fifth apart. This instrument is still in use, but its legendary origin goes back, some say, more than five thousand years.*

right playing the part of a fingerboard, which would have allowed the strings to be shortened at will, the range of the instrument being extended in consequence; if this was the case, the *crwth* would have been an instrument of plucked strings, and could not, therefore, be considered as an ancestor of the violin.

However that may be, the fundamental characteristics of the violin existed in some European instruments from the Middle Ages. In 1774 Martin Gerber published his *De cantu et musica sacra*, making use of documents from the Abbey of St. Blaise in the Black Forest. In it he reproduced documents copied in a manuscript of AD 600 and in another 'a little more recent.' One of his drawings shows a pear-shaped bowed monochord. This instrument, with very limited

LEFT   *The eleventh-century* crouth *with three strings is a bowed instrument. An ancestor of the Welsh crouth, it existed in France before the Crusades. Its possibilities were very limited. Nothing is known of its tuning.*

RIGHT   *The Welsh six-stringed* crouth *as it appeared at the end of the eighteenth century, when it was still in use. It has four strings for the bow, and two strings plucked with the thumb of the left hand. The strings were evidently not co-planar; the top of the bridge, being arched, allowed only one string to be touched at a time.*

The lira of the Hortus deliciarum. *It is the same instrument as the one in the preceding figure. The proximity of the convent in the Black Forest to the one in Alsace where Herrad of Landsberg wrote his work probably explains the resemblance.*

possibilities, was intended to accompany the ancient plainchant; since its intervals were never greater than a sixth, the monochord sufficed to keep the cantors accurate. In any case, it must have been in common use, since we find exactly the same model in the famous *Hortus deliciarum*, the Alsatian manuscript drawn up between 1175 and 1185 by Herrad of Landsberg, for the instruction of the nuns in the Convent of St. Odilia. This instrument was then called *lira*, which seems to have been the generic name for all bowed instruments in the Middle Ages. Their musical possibilities were very restricted; in German dialect the word *lire* (*leier* in German) has remained synonymous with monotonous repe-

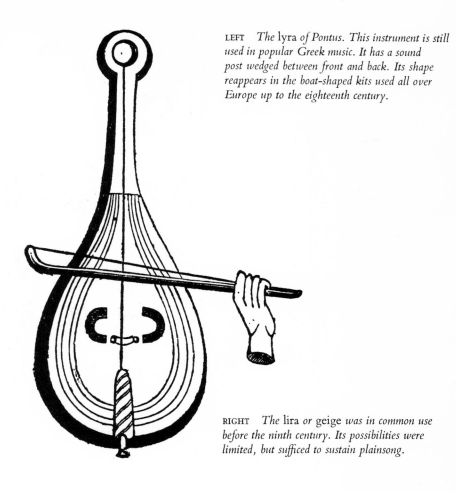

LEFT *The lyra of Pontus. This instrument is still used in popular Greek music. It has a sound post wedged between front and back. Its shape reappears in the boat-shaped kits used all over Europe up to the eighteenth century.*

RIGHT *The* lira *or* geige *was in common use before the ninth century. Its possibilities were limited, but sufficed to sustain plainsong.*

tition. The Greeks of Pontus still use the *lyra* now, an instrument which Praetorius describes exactly (except for the pegs) in his work. This Greek *lyra* has three strings tuned in fourths:

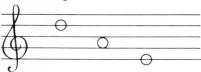

The instrument has a smooth fingerboard and players place their fingers on the strings as our violinists do. According to Mr. Anoyanakis of Athens, who kindly supplied the information on this point, it is quasi-standardized in its shape and dimensions.[1]

The total length of the Greek *lyra* is about 50 cm (19¾ inches), while that of the violin is 58 cm (about 22¾ inches). The back is flat and the front arched; there is no bass bar, but there is a sound post similar to that of the violin, fitted between the front and the back.

The instrument comes straight from the Middle Ages. The sound post was common to the various bowed instruments. All these ancient instruments had at the most three strings (probably tuned in fourths) and gave rise, with the appearance of ligatures (or frets) to the family of viols. The ancient English fiddlers played similar instruments with four strings, and the difficulty of wield-

English geige. *In the eleventh century* geiges *had four strings. The instrument was still pear-shaped, but the increase in the number of strings was soon to lead to the introduction of incurved sides to allow free passage for the bow in playing.*

[1] Cf. Anoyanakis, 'Survivances de l'ancienne rythmique dans la musique populaire grecque,' *Cahiers d'art* (Paris, 1957), pp. 247–55.

ing the bow with instruments of this shape was soon to lead to the introduction of incurved sides in all bowed instruments.

As early as the thirteenth century, Jerome of Moravia described the *rubera*, an instrument with two strings tuned a fifth apart and played with a bow, which gave ten notes corresponding to the diatonic scale used in the Middle Ages. Unfortunately no drawing has been preserved.

In the fourteenth century the *rebec*, also called *ribeca* or *rebecchino*, appeared, obviously derived from the Arab *rebab*. Rebecs have existed in various sizes, and they have also been called *geiges* in some places. The rebec, the shape of which has not yet been stabilized, has been used for folklore music in different regions down to our own times. It is a popular instrument above all else. It has a smooth

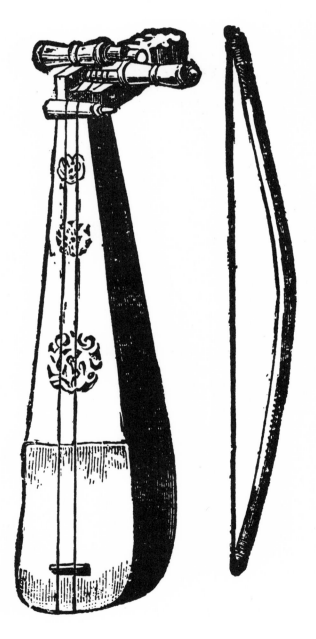

The *rebab*, *ancestor of the rebec. This instrument, with two or three strings, was still used among the Arabs and in Egypt in the last century. The model at left dates from the end of the nineteenth century. Its resemblance to the rebec is quite striking.*

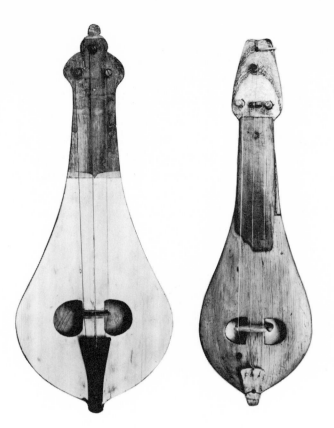

Two types of rebec as still used in Greece. This characteristic shape is found in many carvings from the Middle Ages. All the essential elements of the violin are already present, except the bass bar.

fingerboard over which are stretched three strings tuned in fifths. It is still used in Greece, especially in the islands. Two types of rebec of different shapes are illustrated here; these instruments are made by the players themselves, with dimensions adapted to the physical proportion of each musician. The total length varies from 46 cm (about 18 inches) to 43 cm (about 17 inches); the length of the strings from 25 cm (about 10 inches) to 30 cm (about $11\frac{3}{4}$ inches). These strings are tuned like those of the violin (E–A–D), or else formerly – and in some islands still – in the following way:

(the third string being the octave of the previous D). The fingerboard is smooth. The back is always vaulted. Back, neck, and head are made out of one piece of wood, resistant to humidity (wild mulberry, wild pear tree, chestnut, plum tree), while the front is made from pine wood.

The interior structure is curious and deserves to be explained because ancient documents give us no precise information on this acoustically important point. The left foot of the bridge rests on the front near the left sound hole, but the right foot rests directly upon the sound post, supported by the back, through the sound hole. This arrangement can be justified from the acoustic standpoint:

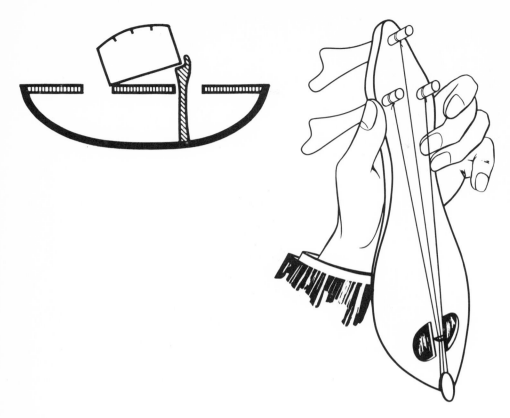

a system is sought which offers a twofold degree of freedom, the low strings stirring a relatively supple front and the high string reacting upon the much more rigid back.

The playing of the Greek rebec offers an interesting peculiarity: the musician does not press the strings on the fingerboard as the violinist does, but pushes them sideways with his nail to produce a special sonorous effect.

To sum up, we know that the lyre and rebec have never had more than three strings, and that only in 1511 did incurved sides appear, allowing the use of a greater number of strings. Sebastian Virdung, in his *Musica getutscht*, divides string instruments into several categories; after describing instruments with a keyboard, he says:

The other kind of string instrument has no keys, but ligatures or other lines or marks [on the neck] so that the notes can be produced very accurately by resting the strings on frets, which allows the instrument to be tuned and the method of playing it to be explained. The following instruments are of this type.

Die ander Art der saitespil dyeselben haben nit schlüssel. Aber bünde un sunst gewisezile oder gemercke, do man sicher griff mag haben. Als uff den koren und bünden, nach welchem man dieselben auch mag regulieren und beschreiben daruff zu lernen. Als dise instrument haben die hernach folgen.

The author then mentions lyres, lutes, and gitterns, *lyra, lauten, quintern*. It will be noted that the lyre here is the original hurdy-gurdy, an *organistrum*.

LEFT   *The large geige. Virdung's illustration is from 1511. The instrument has frets: it is a viol. Incurved sides are definitely adopted.*

RIGHT   *The small geige shown by Virdung. This is the rebec, as found at the time of Praetorius.*

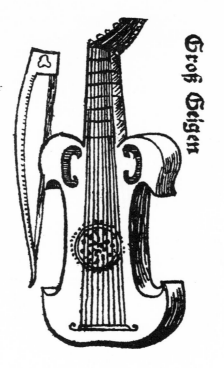

Groß Geigen

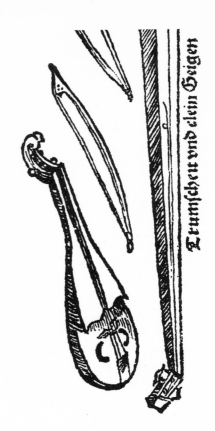

Trumſcheit und clein Geigen

Virdung continues:

The third kind of musical instrument also has frets, thanks to which it is possible to tune them and to teach the art of using them, as in the following instruments.

Dye dritt art der saitenspile dye haben auch köre der saiten und nach denselben kören mag man sye auch regulieren und beschreiben daruff zu lerne, als dye nachfolgende instrument synd.

The author gives as an example the large geige (*gross geigen*), an ancestor of the viol, with a bow and numerous strings.

Finally Virdung describes another sort of instrument:

The fourth kind of instrument has no frets, and has only one or two strings, or three in most models, but never more. As they cannot be tuned, and therefore taught, so precisely, training and talent in melodic appreciation are much more necessary for their mastery than rules. Therefore I will say least of all about these instruments, since I maintain and consider that they are useless; the same applies to small geiges (cleynen geigen) and the marine trumpet.

Die fiert art der saitenspill, die haben nit bünden auch nure ynen oder zwei kore, oder drey uff das maiste, und nit darüber. Darumb sye nit so eygentliche zu regulieren und zu beschrybens ynd, daruff zu lernen, Dan das muss vil mere durch grosse übung, un durch den verstand des gesangs zu gan dann man das durch regeln beschryben mag. Darumb ich von denselben instrumenten an dem aller mynsten wirt schryben, dann ich sie auch für on nütze instrumenta achte un halte, als dye cleynen geigen und das Trumscheit.

In 1528 Martin Agricola in his *Musica Instrumentalis*, published in Wittenberg, reproduced exactly the small geige (*clein geige*) of Virdung; it is the classic rebec. Thus, the bowed instruments in general use at the beginning of the sixteenth century are of two essential types: the large geige (*gross geige*) of Virdung, which is also found in Agricola's work and which is the direct ancestor of the viols, and the *clein geige* (small geige, rebec), for which Agricola has no esteem.

The question of large geiges and small geiges is also raised in 1618 in the *Syntagma musicum* of Michael Praetorius (112), in which the plates are of exceptional interest since they provide a scale. We learn there that the rebec measures about 42 cm (16½ inches), neck included, while the violin measures 58 cm (about 22¾ inches). Our present violin is called 'real descant violin,' *rechte Discant Geig*; the tenor (no. 5) was still in use at the time of Stradivari; lastly the *bass Geig* is the ancient church double bass (length of body about 85 cm (33½ inches), compared with 75 cm (about 29½ inches) for our present cello).[2] In short, the rebec was in general use from the thirteenth century; by 1620 it had hardly changed: it had a pear-shaped body of reduced size, three strings tuned in fifths, a smooth fingerboard. At the beginning of the sixteenth century the word 'violin,' *violino*, appears at last.

Etymologically, *violino* is the diminutive of *viola* and means 'little viol.' The name is found after 1529; among other contributors, we find under the name of Gio Battista d'Oneda, mention of '*fa di violino*' (51).

The French name *violon* – which is not the exact translation of *violino* – comes from Provence and, according to Coutagne, passed into French well before the sixteenth century. In any case, it appears in 1529 among the accounts of Francis I (cf. H. Prunières, *Musique de chambre de François Ier*). At this period, violinists were ranked as domestics; the lute and the viol remained pastimes for the nobility.

Although the term *violon* exists from this period, we know nothing accurate about the structure of the instrument, and we cannot assert that the *violon* at the time of Francis I was exactly like our modern violin, which was only perfected later by various instrument makers, especially the Italians. During the last century it was maintained that the creator of our present instrument was Gasparo Da Salo, maker of viols, who also constructed violins, some models of which have come down to us. But it is now known that Da Salo was born in 1540, and, because of that very fact, cannot be the inventor of the instrument in question. Other authors, Peluzzi, Foffa, attribute the invention of the violin to the lute maker Zanetto da Montichiaro or Pellegrino. According to Peluzzi, this lute maker, born about 1522, would have followed the advice of the mathematician Tartaglia in elaborating the new instrument. But the foundation for this statement, a letter from the Chapter of the Church at Brescia, dated 1552, is very slight. It is now known that the lute maker Andreas Amati constructed a violin as early as 1546, but it is not possible to declare from that fact

---

[2] I translate *Geig* as *violin*; the word *Geige*, from which the French 'gigue' is clearly derived, is still used in Germany today for the violin, as well as *Violine* and *Fiedel*.

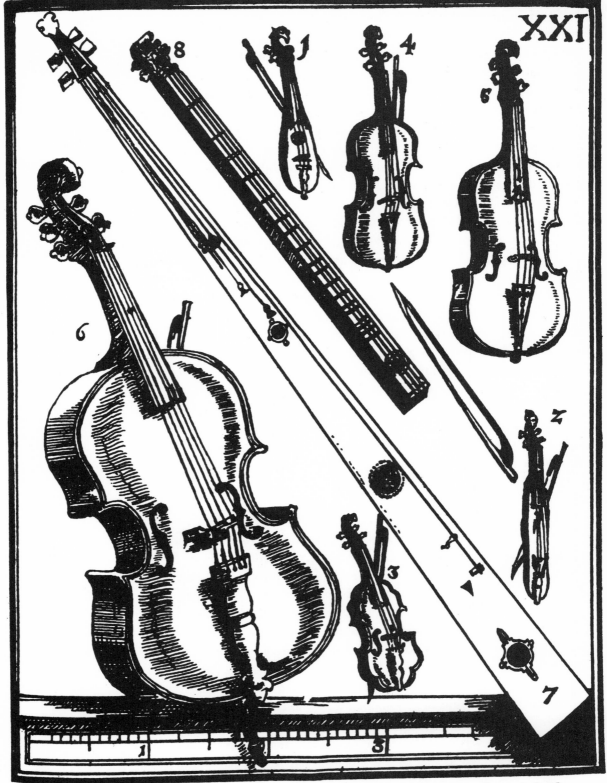

XXI

1.2. Kleine Posche, Geigen, ein Octav höher. 3. Discant-Geig, ein Quart höher.
4. Rechte Discant-Geig. 5. Tenor-Geig. 6. Bass-Geig de bracio. 7. Trumscheidt.
8. Scheidtholt.

alone that Amati was the first to make such an instrument. Originally it also had three strings; it was a rebec with the body of a viol (*lyra da braccio* of Praetorius).

We know nothing certain, therefore, about the violin before 1550, beyond the fact that there appeared fairly suddenly at the beginning of the sixteenth century a new instrument which was rapidly to supplant the rebec because of its extraordinary qualities adapted to the needs of fiddlers: a clearer sound, powerful enough to eventually allow its being played in the open air, and a wider range.

In 1556 appears the text of Philibert Jambe-de-Fer, giving at last a precise description of the classic violin, which thus enters history.

We know little of its author. It is presumed that he was born at La Fere or Lyons. He probably lived at Poitiers, where he published *Cent psalmes de David* in 1549. He perished in the massacre of Protestants on Saint Bartholomew's Day at Lyons in 1572. Mention of him appears in the *Chronique lyonnaise* of Jean Guéraud (1536–62); he was at that time a musician of repute. He wrote a small work: *Epitome musical des tons, sons et accords des voix humaines, fleustes d'alleman, fleustes a neuf trois, violes et violons*, which was printed in Lyons by Michel du Bois in 1556, the only known copy of which is in the Bibliothèque du Conservatoire, Paris. It will be of interest to quote *in extenso* the passage in this book concerning bowed instruments, viols and violins, on page 21, in the chapter *L'accord et le ton du violon*:

The violin is very unlike the viol; first, it has only four strings, which are tuned in fifths one from the other, and in each of the said strings there are four tones, so that in the four strings there are as many tones as the viol has in five. It has a smaller, flatter body and produces a much less refined sound; there are no frets because the fingers touch as it were from tone to tone in all the parts. They are tuned in unison, that is the treble is tuned to the lowest open string; the bass part is tuned to the highest open string; the tenors and countertenors to the second lowest string near the drone string; and they call it 'G (sol)–D (a second above C)' all together; moreover the said French violin is no different from the Italian as far as playing goes.

Why do you call some viols and the others violins? We call viols those which gentlemen, merchants, and other people of quality play as a pastime. The Italians call them viol da gamba because they are held low, some between the legs, others on some seat or stool, others on the knees, especially by the aforesaid Italians; the French use this method very little.

The other kind is called violin and is the one commonly used for dancing, and with good reason: because it is easier to tune, since the fifth resounds more sweetly

Le violon est fort contraire à la viole; premier, il n'a que quatre cordes, lesquelles s'accordent à la quinte de l'une à l'autre et en chacune desdites cordes y a quatre tons, en sorte et manierè qu'en quatre cordes il a autant de tons que la viole en a en cinq. Il est en forme de corps plus petit, plus plat et beaucoup plus rude en son; il n'a nulle taste par ce que les doigts se touchent quasi de ton en ton en toutes les parties. Ils prennent leurs tons et accords tous à unisson à savoir le dessus prend le sien à la plus basse corde à vuide. Le bas prend le sien à la chanterelle à vuide; les tailles et hautes-contres prennent le leur à la seconde d'embas, près le bourdon, et l'appellent G sol ré ut le second, tous ensemble au reste le dit violon ne diffière en rien le françoys avec l'italien en c'est instrument quant au jeu.

Pourquoi appelez-vous violes les unes et les autres violons? Nous appelons violes celles desquelles les gentilz hommes marchantz et autres gens de Vertuz passent leur temps. Les Italiens les appellent viole da gambe par ce qu'elles se tiennent en bas, les uns entre les jambes, les autres sur quelque siège ou escabeau, autres sur les genoux mesme les ditz Italiens; les Français ont bien peu en usage cette façon.

L'autre sorte s'appelle violon et c'est

in the ear than the fourth. It is also easier to carry, and this is very important especially when conducting a wedding or a mummery.

The Italians call it violin da brascia or violone because it is held on the arm; by some with a scarf, tape, or something like that; the bass, on account of its weight, is very difficult to carry and is therefore supported by a little hook in an iron ring or something similar, which is attached very neatly to the back of the said instrument, in such a way as not to impede the player. I have drawn you no figure of the said violin, because you can consider it like the viol, and besides, except for those who earn their living by it, few people play it. The lines in the example show the strings of the said instruments and the figures show the frets.

Now, then, you are in tune if the string does not break. Play the gamba a little; yes indeed, sir, we recommend it to you.

'Gamba' is an Italian dance and also means 'leg.'

celuy du quel l'on use en dancerie communément et à bonne cause: car il est plus facile d'accorder, pour ce que la quinte est plus douce à ouyr que n'est la quarte. Il est aussi plus facile à porter, qui est chose fort nécessaire, mesme en conduisant quelques noces ou mommerie.

L'Italien l'appelle violon da brascia ou violone, par ce qu'il se soutient sus les bras; les uns avec escharpe cordons, ou autre chose, le bas à cause de sa pesanteur est fort malaysé à porter, pour autant est soustenu avec un petit crochet dans un aneau de fer, ou d'autre chose, lequel est attaché au doz dudict instrument bien proprement; à celle fin qu'il n'empesche celuy qui en joue. Je ne vous ai mis en figure ledict violon par ce que le pouvez considérer sus la viole, joint qu'il se trouve peu de personnes qui en use, si non ceux qui en vivent par leur labeur.

Les lignes de l'exemple nous représentent les cordes des dictz instruments et les nombres de chiffre nous représentent les tastes.

Or sus doncques, vous voyla d'accord si la corde ne rompt, touchez un peu la Gambe, ouy dea monsieur nous vous la recommandons.

Gambe est une gaillarde italienne et se prend aussi pour jambe.

This quotation calls for a few comments:

1   It gives us a clear description of the violin. The instrument has four strings tuned in fifths one from the other; the body is flatter and smaller than that of the viol; the sound is less refined (has greater power) than that of the viol, and the instrument has *nulle taste*, that is, no fret, limiting the tones. The useful vibrating length of the string is about the same as that of the present violin (32.5 cm, about $12\frac{3}{4}$ inches) since the author points out that the fingers *touch as it were from tone to tone.*

The complete quartet is composed as follows:

the treble   our violin
the countertenor   our viola
the tenor   very large viola
the bass   our double bass

In the absence of a diapason, the violinist stretched the low string until the instrument gave the correct sound. The player of the bass then tuned his first string to the low string of the violin (G). The viola and the large viola took the same note for the *second lowest string near the drone string* (therefore these two instruments were tuned like the present viola). In short, only the tuning of the bass was a tone lower than the present cello. It will be noted also that the composition of the quartet, with the large viola, was more logical. The tuning 'G (sol)–D (a second above C)' is certainly our present-day G tuning, as the works of Virdung, Fogliani, and others show.

2   *Au reste ledit violon suyt de point en point la viole.* (*Moreover the said violin follows the viol in every respect.*) The violin was played like the viol, of which it possessed the essential features. Jambe-de-Fer indicates this again further on: 'Je ne vous ai mis en figure ledict violon par ce que le pouvez considérer sur la viole.' ('I have drawn you no figure of the said violin, because you can consider it like the viol.') The absence of a figure, an absence intended by the writer, may be regretted in this particular case, but other documents fill the gap.

In 1556, the violin was a new invention, since *few people play it,* except fiddlers; that is why it is considered useless to speak of it at length.

3   *... ne diffère en rien le françoys avec l'italien ... quant au jeu.* (*the ... French violin is no different from the Italian as far as playing goes.*) This statement settles an old dispute: is the violin of French or of Italian origin? It depends on which violin is being referred to, and it is certain that both types were in common use in 1556. The two types were in no wise different *as far as playing goes,* that is, as to instrumental technique. If the two instruments were different, where did the difference lie? Since Jambe-de-Fer says himself that he does not sketch the violin because it can be considered *like the viol,* it is certain that the difference is in the dimensions varying from one model to another. Other documents confirm this point; Lesure has already pointed out that violins made in the 'Paris style' and in the 'Italian style,' from Venice, Brescia, Cremona, etc. have long been in use.

4   *Nous appelons violes celles desquelles les gentilz hommes marchantz et autres gens de vertuz passent leur temps.* (*We call viols those which gentlemen, merchants, and other people of quality play as a pastime.*) It is obvious that the instrument for educated people was the viol. The use of the violin was left to 'those who earn their living by it ... conducting a wedding or a mummery.' Therefore, in 1556, the violin is currently used by fiddlers, who abandon the rebec. After carrying out research in the archives of Lyons, Dr. Coutagne observed: 'Our archives mention a great many popular musicians at this epoch; now it is to be noted that while we find mention of *fiddlers, taborins, rebecquets* or *rebec players* in Lyons during the first half of the sixteenth century, these professional names fall out as soon as the word *violin* appears in our records, and some musicians whose names occur over a long period are called by one of the first names until about 1550, but exclusively by the last name after that date.' Everything suggests therefore that the violin appeared in Lyons through a sudden change in the rebec family about 1550. At this date the violin definitely replaced the

rebec. I have discovered in the archives of the same city another record revealing that a certain Lejeune, an instrument maker of Lyons, was making violins there before 1558.

5   *L'Italien l'appelle violon da brascia.* (*The Italians call it viol da brascia.*) *Viol da brascia* has given the word Bratsche in Germany, which still indicates the viola of the quartet of stringed instruments. In 1723 Filippo Bonanni, in his *Gabinetto armonico*, states that the *violino* is a large instrument.

The hypothesis that the instruments of the Italian quartet were larger than the French instruments of the same name is confirmed once more by the precise details concerning the Italian manner of holding the instruments: '[The Italian instruments] are held ... on some seat or stool, others on the knees ... the French use this method very little.' The present violin is easily held under the chin. It was not the same with an instrument considerably larger like the 'Italian violin'; this was rested on a stool or on the knees. In his score of *Orpheus*, 1607, Monteverdi confirms the differences of size, expressly recommending the use of *duoi piccoli violini alla francese*.

If Jambe-de-Fer thus gives many indications about the violin played in Lyons in the middle of the sixteenth century, another Lyonese document supplies further interesting information about the shape of the body. This is the famous portrait of the instrument maker Duiffoprugcar.

DUIFFOPRUGCAR

Several musicographers mention this instrument maker as early as 1812, but in 1893 Dr. Henry Coutagne made him the subject of an historical study which is based on the archives of the city of Lyons.

People have often claimed him as the inventor of the violin. Gaspar Duiffoprugcar belonged to a famous family of instrument makers. The handiwork of several of them – usually lutes or viols – is to be found in various museums. The family name Tieffenbrucker, pronounced in the German Swabian dialect, was written down by French scribes as Duiffoprugcar, Duiffoproucar, Dutfontbrocguard, Diffobricard, Desfobrical, etc. The act of naturalization granted to the instrument maker by Henry II in January 1558 in Paris calls him 'nostre cher et bien amé Caspar Dieffenbrugar, Alleman, faiseur de lutz, natif de Fressin, ville impériale en allemaigne' ('our dearly beloved Caspar Dieffenbrugar, a German, a lute maker, a native of Fressin, the imperial city in Germany'). Some authors have given him a Tyrolian origin, confusing Freising, spelt Fressin, with Füessen, but the act of naturalization discovered by Henry Coutagne destroys this hypothesis. The date of Duiffoprugcar's birth is given on the portrait engraved by Woeiriot, which bears the inscription: *Aeta. ann.* XLVIII 1562. Aged forty-eight in 1562, Duiffoprugcar must have been born in 1514.

After an apprenticeship in his own country, he probably went to Northern Italy, where several members of his family were already working. It is thought that he frequented the workshop of an instrument maker at Bologna. His presence is noted in Lyons in 1533, and in 1544 his marriage is registered at Füessen to the daughter of a merchant of that city. He was back in Lyons before 1553, but little else is known for certain. Coutagne mentions someone of the same name as having frequented the fairs of Lyons, before settling at Lucerne in Switzerland, where the records mention him in 1571. His marriage at Füessen is hardly in accordance with a document in the archives of 1567, mentioning 'Gaspard Dutfondbrocguard faiseur de leutz et ... Barbe Homeau, sa femme.' The wife of Duiffoprugcar would therefore have been of French origin, unless this refers to a second marriage, an hypothesis which other documents seem to confirm.

However that may be, Duiffoprugcar was settled in Lyons by 1553 at the latest; the act of naturalization in 1588 states: 'Il y a ja longtemps qu'il a laissé ledict lieu de sa nativité pour venir se habiter en nostre ville de Lyon.' ('He left his birthplace long ago to come and live in our city of Lyons'). It has been put forward that Duiffoprugcar came to France at the request of Francis I, and this is not impossible. Lyons was then well on the way to becoming the 'capital of Gaul'; crafts were exercised freely there, and countless artists and scholars of all nationalities were attracted there.

Duiffoprugcar must have succeeded in business in Lyons. When his house was expropriated and demolished at the time of the construction of the citadel, the king's architects valued it at the then large sum of 9,245 pounds. This, however, was the beginning of the instrument maker's ruin, because he never received compensation.

A document in the archives[3] shows that Duiffoprugcar, a Protestant, was subjected to a seizure of property. On September 28, 1570, the authorities confiscated eight lutes, probably a large portion of his stock, and an authentic deed was drawn up. Therefore he was still alive. Ruined by the loss of his house, despoiled as a Protestant, Duiffoprugcar died between September 1570 and December 1571.

Several documents in the archives concern the disputes of his heirs over the sum which should have been paid to them in compensation for the dispossession inflicted on their father. They mention a quarter of the sum as being due to his

---

[3] Rhone Archives, Series E: 3E 4499-Dorlin, *Carnet de la foire d'aoust 1570*, p. 185, interesting from several points of view. We read there:

On September 28, 1570 – Dufobrucard – Levy by order in writing – In the presence of myself, Claude Ponnet ... that Mr. Jehan Brissac, in charge of the levy and to enforce the payment of the sums resulting from the rent of houses and properties of those of the new religion in this city, entered the shop of Gaspard Dufobrucard, master maker of lutes ... in which for the payment or advance of the rent of the same, he took and carried away eight lutes, mounted and ready for playing, which he delivered and gave into the custody of Mr. Barth-y Dusocheys, royal notary of the said Lyons of which matters the said Fobrucard asked for a deed ...	*Du vingt huitième jour du moys de sp-bre l'an mil cinq cens soixante dix. – Dufobrucard – Levée en papier – En la p-nce de moy Claude Ponnett ... que Me Jehan Brissac commis à la levée et à contraindre à payer les den. provenans des louages des maisons et héritages de ceux de la nouvelle relligion en ceste ville est entré en la bouticque de Gaspard Dufobrucard M-e faiseur de luch ... en laquelle pour le payment ou avancement du louage d'icelle il a prins et empourté huict pièces de luch montez et pretz à jouer lesquelz il a baillez et remis en garde à M-r Barth-y Dusocheys notaire royal dud. Lyon desquelles choses led. Fobrucard a demandé acte ...*

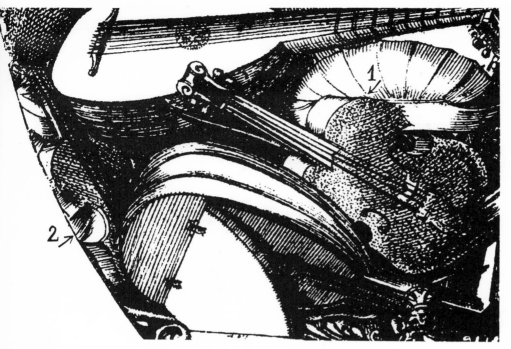

children 'Symon, Gérémye, and Jehan Duifoprocard, heirs of the late Gaspard Duifoprocard and also Marguerite Duifobrocard, brothers and sister.' There is also question of a proceedings opened against 'Gaspard Duyfoprocard tuteur et curateur' (tutor and guardian) of three children still minors, by a German grocer Sebastian Hieberlin, husband of Marguerite, and settled in Lyons.[4]

This Gaspard Duiffoprugcar 'tuteur et curateur' is most probably the eldest son of the instrument maker. Coutagne mentions a deed of 1557 which declares that at this time Duiffoproucar lived near 'his son-in-law Valoys Doloy.' One has the impression that the instrument maker had had two children by a first marriage (Gaspard, the eldest, and a daughter married to Valoys Doloy), and that by a second marriage (to Barbe Homeau), he had four other children, three of whom were minors at the time of his death. At any rate it is certain that his eldest son, Gaspard Duiffoprugcar, came to settle in Paris in 1575 as 'master maker of instruments,' and that he was still there in 1582.

An interesting document in the archives, dated September 7, 1559, tells us that the lute maker of Lyons prosecuted one of his co-workers named Lejeune for counterfeit and for using a false mark. Lejeune, who was sent to prison, is called 'maker of gitterns, zithers, violins, and other instruments.' Duiffoprugcar is given as 'master maker of the said gitterns, zithers, and other instruments.'

The portrait of the lute maker engraved by Pierre Woeiriot takes on all its significance in the light of Jambe-de-Fer's text. Duiffoprogcar was first of all a 'faiseur de leutz.' He is seen in the engraving holding a measuring compass

---

[4] Thanks to the kind suggestions of Mr. Tricou, Notary of Lyons, whose father had studied the personal history of Duiffoprugcar, I have found many unpublished documents in the Rhone Archives.

(used to determine the place of the frets) in his right hand; in his left, he holds an unfinished lute. Before him lie the various instruments made in his workshop. We can see several lutes, a small harp, a zither, a gittern, and some bowed instruments, including a viol, two violins, and a rebec.

The viol shown has five strings, as in Jambe-de-Fer's description of the 'violon da brascia.' The instrument has five frets (therefore it was tuned in fourths, each fret giving a semitone); the ribs are high; the sound holes have the *f* shape, the bridge is placed below the sound holes. The shape of the body is hybrid between the viol (curves of the upper part, near the neck) and the present violin (lower part of the instrument). The head has a scroll similar to that of the present violin. The dimensions of the body bear some relation to the size of the lute, i.e. about 42 cm (16½ inches). The instrument corresponds in dimensions to the present viola.

In the picture, the first violin, which is seen in full and from the front, is the Italian violin described by Jambe-de-Fer: 'very unlike the viol; ... four strings ... smaller, flatter body ... no frets ... easier to carry ...' The sound holes of this instrument are the classic ones of the eighteenth-century viol; the bridge is in the normal place, as on our violin; the body has the characteristic corners of the violin; the pegs are placed as on our present violin and the head is in the scroll form. On the extreme left of the engraving, in the background, there is another instrument with four strings. It is partly hidden, but the left half is fully visible. This is the French violin which 'few people play,' and it is noteworthy that the lute maker wished it to be seen among the instruments he constructed.

Finally, beneath the viol we can see another instrument, the body of which also has the shape of the present violin. The sound holes have a special shape. Fitted with three strings, the instrument is smaller than the violin; it is an exact reproduction of the rebec in its perfected shape, dating from the beginning of the sixteenth century.

Certain details of violin structure had not been standardized in that period; for example, the sound holes were shaped according to the fancy of each instrument maker. Woeiriot's engraving, however, proves that 'the instrument with four strings and four corners,' with a smooth fingerboard and dimensions smaller than those of the viol, was in common use in Lyons by 1562, when Duiffoprugcar was forty-eight years old.

In conclusion, nothing allows us to attribute the invention of the violin to Duiffoprugcar with any certainty, but this instrument maker of renown and talent was certainly one of those who established the use of the present violin with the dimensions it has now. Thus the French origin of the present instrument is supported first of all by the personality of the lute maker of Lyons, by various allusions found in documents, like the recommendation of Monteverdi which has already been cited, and especially by the information supplied by Praetorius, as well as by some considerations concerning the technique of moulds.

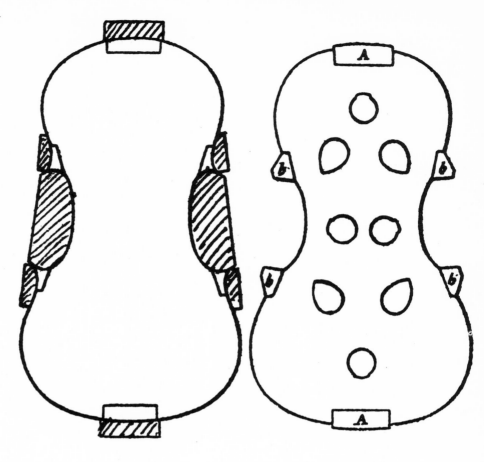

THE VARIETY OF MOULDS

The examination of this particular point in the making of violins offers interesting information about the French origin of the present violin. The violin is usually constructed on a *mould*; this is a board 2 cm (about ¾ of an inch) thick, cut to the interior shape of the instrument, which decides its shape and dimensions. In our own day, moulds are established by a copy of classic models, but it was not always so. The ancient instrument makers used geometrical calculations to design their models.[5]

The shape was worked out by a calculation of proportions, starting from a basic *modulus*. This method was probably the result of mathematical specula-

[5] In his *Harmonie Universelle*, published in 1636, Father Mersenne describes the method of barring a lute:

The table is barred by being divided into eight equal parts, so as to glue its six bars on the second, third, fourth, fifth, sixth, and seventh division, because the neck begins on the eighth division, beyond the table. As to the rose, it must be so placed that its centre comes on the fifth division, on which is glued the fourth bar. As to the bridge, to which all the strings are attached, it is placed between the first and second parts of the table, because, having divided these two parts into three other equal parts, the said bridge is glued on to the second part from the bottom. ... But it should be noticed that the neck or fingerboard must be of the same length as the distance from the beginning of the table to the middle of the rose, which means that the neck must have five parts and the table eight, so that it forms the proportion of the minor sixth with the said neck, so that there is nothing which is not harmonic in the lute.

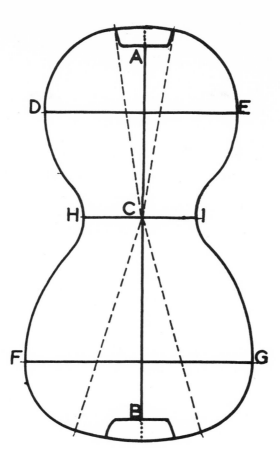

The geometry of the violin is determined from a modulus given by the interior length of the body. This produces DE = AB/2; HI = AB/3; FG = AB(5/8).

tions on music, of which the division of the monochord, achieved by Pythagoras, is the prototype.[6] The entire form of the instrument was determined according to the harmonic divisions of the sonometer.

Having had occasion to study ancient moulds, I have noted that they have been designed with ruler and compass. On the other hand, geometrical analysis of the shape of the violin has shown us that it can be reconstructed by a series of connected arcs of a circle. We can verify the following proportions: Modulus AB = length of mould = length of the vibrating string. This is the unit. By dividing the modulus AB by 2, we get the width DE. The width of the lower part (FG) is equal to DE × 5/4; the width of the middle (HI) is equal to the modulus divided by 3.

It is not impossible that mathematicians, adepts in geometry, or theoreticians of music may have contributed to the perfecting of musical instruments. In Northern Italy, scholars like Tartaglia, who died in 1557, and Cardan, his contemporary, knew how to solve equations of the fourth degree, and applied mathematics to several inventions. It may be presumed that the lute makers of

[6] These notions are clearly set out by Praetorius, who wrote in his *Syntagma musicum*, 1618, concerning the monochord: *For all musical instruments and organs, this must determine the true tone and the proportions, and may rightly be considered as the father of all instruments and of all music; let us remember that it is carried out exclusively by compass work.*

Europe had a common fund of tradition. Once instrument making became a specialty, famous workshops, few in number, must have contained the majority of European makers. The designing of moulds certainly formed part of the training of instrument makers.

Now, although the typical shape of certain instruments appears in different countries, its dimensions vary from place to place. These differences in size are explained when we remember that units of measure varied according to regions.

The mould was determined by dividing a basic modulus; this usually corresponds to the unit of local measure – either to one of its multiples or to a simple fraction. Given that the metrical units varied from one country to another, we know that the dimensions of instruments follow these variations. The European metrical units once in use were the following:

England	:	foot of 0.3048 m	Würtemburg	:	foot of 0.2865 m
Prussia	:	foot of 0.3139 m	Baden, Switzerland	:	foot of 0.30 m
Bavaria	:	foot of 0.2919 m	Austria	:	foot of 0.3161 m
Saxony	:	foot of 0.2832 m	Holland	:	foot of 0.2840 m
Italy (Brescia)	:	1 'arm' = 0.70992 = 12 inches of 0.059 m			
France	:	royal foot 0.324 m = 12 inches of 0.027 m			

The advantages of the duodecimal system may be noticed in passing: 12 is divisible by 2, 3, 4, 6; with 8 we get the simple relation 2/3 and with 9 the relation 3/4. The designing of a mould with the help of duodecimal units thus becomes possible without complicated calculations.

Now we can understand why Jambe-de-Fer distinguishes the Italian violin from the French one. In fact, the violin made in Brescia, using the measures indicated above for determining the mould, would have the following dimensions:

Length AB of the mould	= the modulus = 1/2 'arm' = 35.49 cm
Vibrating length of the strings	= *idem* = 35.49 cm
Exterior length of the instrument of which the mould is 35.49 cm	= 35.49 × 13/12 = 38.44 cm
Width of the top	= 35.49 ÷ 2 = 17.74 cm
Width of the middle	= 35.49 ÷ 3 = 11.83 cm
Width of the lower part	= 17.74 × 5/4 = 22.17 cm

This is the 'large Italian violin' of the sixteenth century. By contrast, with French measurements we get:

Length of string	= 32.4 cm
Length AB of the mould	= 32.4 cm
Full length of the front of the instrument	= 32.4 × 13/12 = 35.1 cm
Width of the top	= 32.4 cm ÷ 2 = 16.2 cm
Width of the lower part	= 16.2 cm × 5/4 = 20.25 cm
Width of the middle	= 32.4 cm ÷ 3 = 10.8 cm

These are precisely the dimensions of our present-day instrument.

The 'plan' of the present violin agrees perfectly only with the old French metrical units. Rather than consider this a coincidence, we may reasonably conclude that the French lute makers played a decisive part in determining the first models of violins. Thus the text of Jambe-de-Fer and the portrait of Duiffoprugcar throw special light upon one another. Besides, other documents focus attention upon Lyons in this matter. In the *Comptes des bâtiments du roi*, the word *violon* occurs on a receipt signed June 23, 1533 at Lyons. It is quite clear why Monteverdi mentions *duoi piccoli violini alla francese* in his *Orpheus* in 1607.

THE VIOLIN DESCRIBED BY PRAETORIUS

The *Syntagma musicum* by Praetorius, published in 1618 at Wolfenbüttel, offers other interesting points of information on the various forms of the violin. In the *Organography* section, Praetorius studies 'all musical instruments, both old and new, foreign, barbarian, and unknown, native, artistic, and pleasing; their intonations and properties, their accurate reproduction, and also organs, ancient and new.' In this book we find carefully engraved plates illustrating instruments, accompanied by a scale which enables us to measure their dimensions accurately. The author also indicates how the instruments are tuned.

In chapter 20, 'Violen, Geigen, Violuntzen,' we read on the subject of viols:

There are two kinds of these ... the viol da gamba and the viol da bracio. ... The instrument makers in the cities [Kunstpfeiffern in Stadten] *distinguish: viols da gamba, called viols, and viols da bracio, called violins (Geige) or Polish violins; perhaps because this type of instrument was first constructed in Poland, or else because there are virtuosi of this instrument in that country.*

Considerations follow about their tuning, playing, etc.

Table of pitch given by Praetorius. The descant viol (violino) is tuned as now (G–D–A–E); we see that the gar klein Geig, the rebec, was tuned in fifths, in two ways: A–E–B, or a tone lower, G–D–A. The curious kleine Discant Geige, tuned a fourth above the violin (C–G–D–A), also called violetta picciola, is a member of the family which has disappeared. The rechte Discantgeig is our present violin in both shape and dimensions.

Chapter 22, on viols da bracio, deserves to be quoted at length.

Viols, viola de bracio, idem violino da brazzo; otherwise called Geige, but Fidel by the people, and spoken of as 'de bracio' because it is held on the arm.

Four strings are given to the following instruments of this type: bass, tenor, and descant violin (this last is called violino, violetta picciola, or also rebecchino); the very small violins have three strings (they are called 'pochette' [kit] in French); they are all tuned in fifths. As these instruments are well known to all, it is useless to speak of them further (except to say that if they are mounted with strings of brass or steel, they produce a sweeter and more pleasing sound than the others).

Viola, Viola de bracio: item, Violino da brazzo; wird sonst eine Geige vom gemeinen Volk aber eine Fidel und daher de bracio genennet, dass sie auf dem Arm gehalten wird.

Derselben Bass-, Tenor- und Discantgeig (welche Violino oder Violetta picciola, auch Rebecchino genennet wird) seind mit 4 Saiten; die gar kleinen Geiglein aber mit drei Saiten bezogen (auf französisch pochette gennant) und werden alle durch quinten gestimmet. Und demnach dieselbige jedermänniglichen bekannt ist, davon (ausser diesem, dass wenn sie mit Messing- und stählenen Saiten bezogen werden, ein stillen und fast lieblichen Resonanz mehr, als die andern, von sich geben) etwas mehr anzudeuten und zu schreiben unnötig.

It is clear, therefore, that the violina (*descant viol*) is our present violin (G–D–A–E); the little descant violin is tuned a fourth higher; finally the *gar klein Geig* with three strings (rebec) is tuned an octave or a ninth above the violin. Plate XXI shows the whole family of 'violins,' instruments without frets, tuned in fifths. We see there the rebec (1) and the kit (2) (tuned an octave higher); the descant violin (3) a fourth higher (this is also the *violetta picciola* of the text); the true violin (4) (*Rechte Discant Geig*) which is exactly our present violin (length of body 35 cm, about 13¾ inches); finally we see the large viola (5), the double bass de bracio (6), and the marine trumpet.

Plate XX shows the viols (instruments with frets), and among them an *italianische Lyra de bracio* with seven strings, the body of which is identical with that of the large viola (same shape, same measurements, same sound holes). This transitional instrument between viol and violin is explicitly said to be of Italian origin. One may therefore conclude that the particular shape of the violin body is of Italian origin. Gaspar Duiffoprugcar had spent some time with Italian instrument makers before settling in Lyons; he had certainly seen some *lyre de bracio*. It would not be surprising if he had tried to improve the rebec by using a body of the *lyra* type adapted to the French regulations insisted upon by the instrument makers at Lyons for whom he worked. In any case, everything goes to confirm that the violin is the result of attempts by makers of viols to improve the rebec, because no one except craftsmen played the violin in Lyons at the beginning of the sixteenth century. Once the violin appeared, the rebec was completely abandoned.

1. 2. 3. Violn de Gamba. 4. Viol Bastarda. 5. Italianische Lyra de bracio.

Viols and violins shown by Praetorius. The curious italianische Lyra de bracio *(5 in the upper illustration) forms the intermediary link between the viols and the violins.*

1 2. Kleine Posch. Geigen, ein Octav höher. 3 Discant -Geig, ein Quart höher
4 Rechte Discant -Geig. 5 Tenor-Geig. 6. Bass-Geig de bracio. 7. Trumscheidt.
8. Scheidtholt.

To sum up, the violin was in common use in 1550, but its shape became stabilized later; it was an accomplished fact by 1618. Father Mersenne wrote in 1636, 'It seems that the sound of the violin is utterly delightful, for those who play it to perfection, like Bocan and Lazarin and several others, soften it at will, and render it inimitable by certain trilling sounds which enchant the listeners.' (*Harmonie universelle*, p. 11)

ATTEMPTS AT PERFECTING THE VIOLIN

Attempts to perfect the violin have all failed. Among others, these are the most interesting:

SAVART, 1791–1841, suggested, with a view to simplification, a body in trapezoid shape, without arches, with straight sound holes, and a bass bar in the middle of the front. In spite of the approval of the Academies of Sciences and of Arts, this modification was never adopted.

CHANOT, 1787–1832, after Savart, imagined a guitar violin, without corners, and having a reversed scroll to make the placing of the strings easier. These were fixed to the front as on the guitar. The sound holes had the form typical of those on viols. The instrument had only an ephemeral success. Chanot's idea has been taken up several times, even recently, but with no further results.

RICHELME, 1833–96, published a small work in 1873: *Renaissance du violon et de ses analogues d'après de nouvelles lois acoustiques plaidant en faveur de la facilité de l'exécution et des grands effets de sonorité.* By means of a 'geometrical composition with full circular curves,' he produced 'a model with a superior timbre and more powerful sonority than any other instrument of the same kind.' I have played a viola made by this craftsmen. The qualities were comparable to those of a normally good instrument; the shift was easy but the great width between the ɔc was an impediment. On the whole, Richelme's instrument was only an insignificant variant of the usual one.

SULEAU took out a patent in 1839 for an instrument with undulated tables. I have played this instrument; its rendering was inferior to that of an average classic violin; the low notes especially were very poor. Suleau also constructed violins with three tables.

TOLBECQUE, at the beginning of the twentieth century, suggested a 'normal violin,' which was similar in all respects to the ordinary instrument, but the sound holes, instead of being out in the front, were replaced by oval holes in the ɔc ribs. The inventor had no illusions over the success of his violin. 'I claim no glory for my invention,' he wrote. 'I only speak of it to put forward an instrument of which the construction rests on a logical concept.' The formula had no more success than the others.

TARLE, 1882–1959, a French doctor, introduced all sorts of modifications to the violin. To the left foot of the bridge he screwed a piece of metal (*vigorine*)

Savart tried to simplify the structure of the violin: trapezoidal shape, no arches, straight sound holes. The instrument's acoustical qualities were inferior to those of the usual violin, especially in the low notes. Experience would show that the shape of the body played only a secondary role in the timbre of the violin.

The violin of Richelme is a variant of the violin, with a simpler geometrical shape. The sketch by Richelme shows that the arcs of the constituent circles are badly joined; the shape is easier to make but is aesthetically less rational.

destined, according to him, to give vigour to the low notes. He made instruments the size of the violin, tuned like the viola and the cello, with a view to lessening the encumbrance of these latter instruments, but it is evident that the standard (i.e. power) of the low notes cannot be sufficient under these conditions without electric amplification. This was achieved later by M. P. Bizos in his 'Superviolins, Stereophonic Violins.' The amplification of the sound of an instrument, captured by microphones of piezoelectric contact, raises delicate problems which have interested many research workers. No satisfactory solution has been found so far.

Perfected versions of the violin are announced periodically and even become the subject of patents, but these attempts seem doomed to failure. The violin appears to resist all modifications, because it has reached a kind of asymptote, in which all the parameters play an optimum role in a complex system of multiple interactions. Well adapted to the human auditive anatomy and psychophysiology, it enables us to obtain with means of extraordinary simplicity – a few pieces of wood and four strings – a practically unlimited multiplicity of effects.

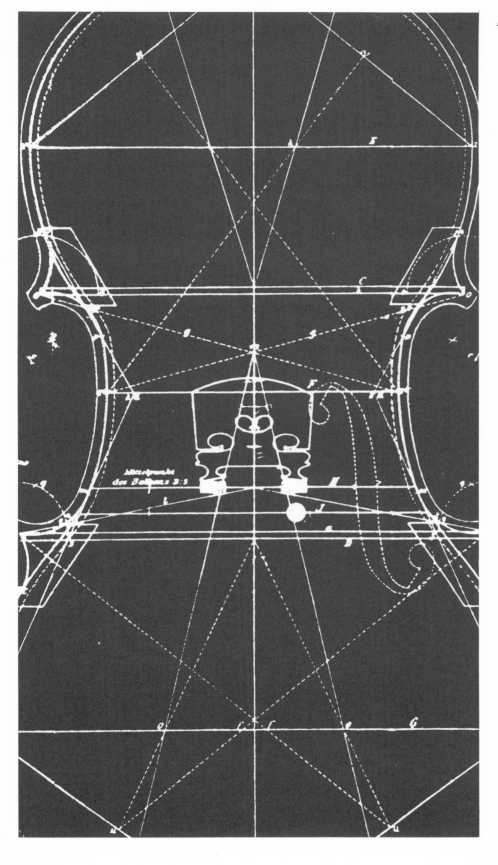

The judgment passed on a shape depends on a series of comparisons between its different elements. In fact, we compare sizes, that is, numbers. The comparison of two numbers gives a relation, and the comparison of two relations supplies a proportion. The study of proportions had become for the Greeks (Plato, Pythagoras) a logical, metaphysical, and aesthetic discipline. The influence of these speculations is noticeable in Greek and Gothic architectural works, and the artists of the Italian Renaissance once again brought these questions to the fore. The idea that 'everything is arranged according to number' soon led to the notion of commensurability between a whole and a part, in architecture as well as in the other spatial arts.

The 'symphonic' conception of a work, taken up again in our own day by various architects and artists, is reflected in the violin, a product of the Renaissance.

USE OF METHODS OF DESIGN

In the *Diversarum artium schedula* by the monk Theophilus, which dates from the twelfth century, we read:

Saddles for horses, eight-man litters, as well as folding chairs, stools, and other things which are carved, must be coated with white, scraped with an iron tool, and then rubbed with shavegrass. ... After that, measure and arrange your work with ruler and compass – that is, pictures and animals or birds and leaves or anything else you want to design. ...

The artist cut out the surface to be decorated with the aid of a compass and according to the ruler so as to arrange the different elements. Makers of musical instruments probably used certain practical aesthetic data known and applied in other crafts.

A fourteenth-century manuscript in the Bibliothèque Nationale, Latin MS 7295, gives the outline of a primitive lute. The shape, designed with ruler and compass, is that of the ovolo, well known in architecture. It is made by four arcs of a circle united, and it has the following peculiarities: it can be executed very easily with the ruler and compass, without a special knowledge of geometry. It can be designed exactly, in all dimensions, starting from the modulus OT: we first draw the big circle from the centre O, then taking A and T as centres, we draw the arcs AB and TC; finally starting from centre D, we finish the ovolo by the arc BNC. It will be seen immediately that, taking as unity the modulus OT, we obtain

$$DT = \sqrt{2}, \quad ND = BD = BT - DT = 2 - \sqrt{2}, \quad NE = 4 - \sqrt{2}$$

so that we can set down the following geometrical relations:

$$\frac{ON}{OE} = \frac{3 - \sqrt{2}}{1} = 1.586..., \quad \frac{NE}{ON} = \frac{4 - \sqrt{2}}{3 - \sqrt{2}} = 1.6333...,$$

irrational representations which approximate the *golden number*. Remembering

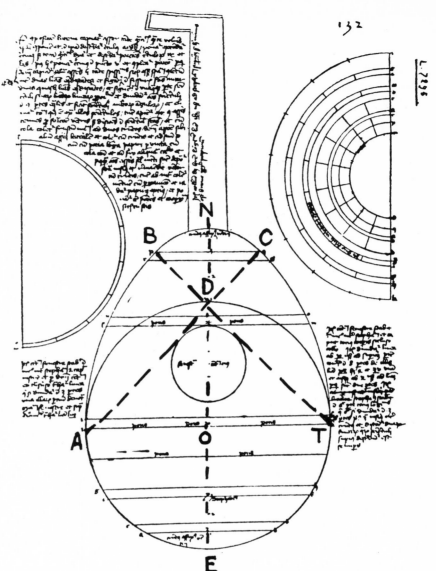

Geometrical design of the lute and model of its ribs after a fourteenth-century Latin manuscript. This figure shows how the ancient makers fashioned the shape of their instruments. The design, made with ruler and compass, is formed by connected circles. The ovolo is a shape particularly adapted to resist deformation; the golden number appears implicitly (place of the centre of the rose and length of the neck). The dotted lines and capital letters have been added to explain the figure.

the exact value of this number 1.618... we see that to within about 2 per cent the centre O of the ovolo divides the length of the table of the lute in the golden proportion.[1]

The length of the neck is not arbitrary either. The relation between the full length of the body and that of the neck is also, according to the original drawing, equal to the golden number. The various parts of the lute are adapted to one another according to the proportion of the golden number, which gives the shape its peculiar harmony.

[1] Or, in ancient language, in 'mean and extreme ratio.' We know the definition of this division: the relation between the full segment (NE) and the large part (ON) equals the relation between the large part and the small one (OE); the common value of these two relations (golden number) is consequently the positive solution of the equation: $x^2 - x - 1 = 0$, or $x = (1 + \sqrt{5}) \div 2$.

In his *Livre de l'art*, Cennino Cennini (1360–1440) gives in chapter 70 the 'measures which the perfectly proportioned human body should have': 'First, as I have told you, divide the face into three parts...'; one of these parts is the modulus serving to measure all the parts of the body, and thus we obtain a 'comodulation' which achieves 'symphonic proportions.'

In 1511 Virdung (142) provides some precise details on the making of instruments, although his actual intention is to teach the art of using them. He says: 'I do not wish to describe how to construct the clavichord and other instruments since that concerns rather architecture and the woodworker's craft than the musician.' At this period, architectural data implied geometrical speculations.

A passage in Father Mersenne's *Harmonie universelle*, 1636 (90), shows that between instrument and neck the proportion of 8/5 (a rational representation near the golden number) was systematically maintained; the centre of the rose was located in the same way. This text shows that technical procedure for generating shapes still existed in Father Mersenne's time.

In 1782 a lute maker, Antonio Bagatella, presented a memoir (7) to the Academy of Sciences, Letters, and Arts on the construction of violins, violas, violoncellos, and double basses. He relates that at the age of nineteen, having damaged his violin and having watched while it was being repaired, he began to be interested in making instruments, and this later turned into a passion. Born probably about 1718, Bagatella had to mend an instrument for Tartini about 1740. In his monograph, Bagatella gives a way of designing the shape of a violin without a model. He divides the length of the front of the instrument

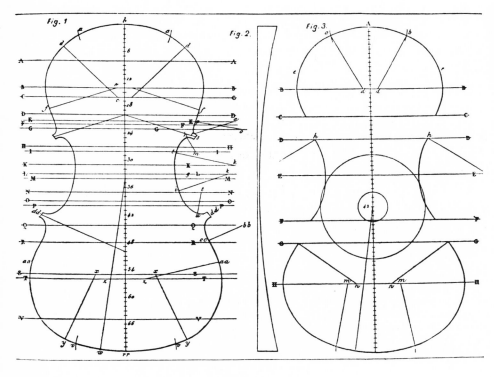

Bagatella's design is an attempt at a geometrical reconstruction of the shape of the classic violin. Note the complexity of the design, based on arbitrary data; the circles are badly joined and the successive arcs have no common centre.

into 72 parts (6 times 12). This division is justified. The length of the violin corresponds to the 6 Cremonese inches, each divided into 12 'points.' Therefore Bagatella's 72 parts are the 72 'points' of Cremona. Starting from this subdivision of the 'modulus,' the author draws a certain number of horizontal lines, and arcs of circles, the centres of which are settled in an arbitrary fashion. He seems to have been groping after centres which would give the best framework for the various classic models of violins (Stradivari, Amati, Stainer, etc.). Then the author indicates three concentric circles, of which the centres are on point 42, for the front, and which correspond, according to him, to the gradation of thicknesses of the back:

Point 42 is the one from which to give the desired thicknesses to the back. To begin with, the compass is opened four and one-third parts, one of its arms is placed on point 42 and a circle is drawn. All the wood within this circle must have a very accurate degree of thickness. ...

As we see, the author indicates how to design the exterior shape of the violin and to draw the thicknesses, but without justifying his method, which in fact has only a very limited interest. The arcs of the circle are not well joined. Moreover, his rule of thicknesses makes no sense, since thickness must depend on the qualities of the wood. Nevertheless Bagatella, a contemporary of Stradivari, used methods which are undoubtedly reminiscent of ancient ones, the meaning of which has been lost. In the middle of the eighteenth century Italian instrument making was in full decline, and to copy existing models was the only method known.

THE SECRETS OF THE GREAT INSTRUMENT MAKERS

The museum of the Conservatoire national de musique in Paris contains a whole series of ancient moulds of instruments, attributed to Stradivari. I have carefully examined these moulds and made an accurate list of their shapes and dimensions. They are moulds of viols and other instruments; they were probably not constructed in Stradivari's workshops, but they are very ancient. One can see clear indications that they were made by ruler and compass calculations. Geometrical analysis of the shape of these moulds shows that numerical proportions were used in designing them.

In his small work *Antonio Stradivari ha parlato*, published in 1941 (107), Peluzzi gives a reproduction of a pasteboard model having the shape of a violin and bearing various inscriptions (*Antonio Stradivari*, 1737, a set of numbers, etc.). One can see the design of a sound hole, the bass bar, the position of the sound post and of the middle of the instrument, and finally three concentric circles similar to those of Bagatella. Peluzzi thinks that the circles provide the key to the radius of the curve of the tables, but that they in no way indicate gradations of thicknesses.

I have carefully examined this pasteboard, which is now in the possession of Bisiach, an instrument maker of Milan. Its authenticity seems doubtful for

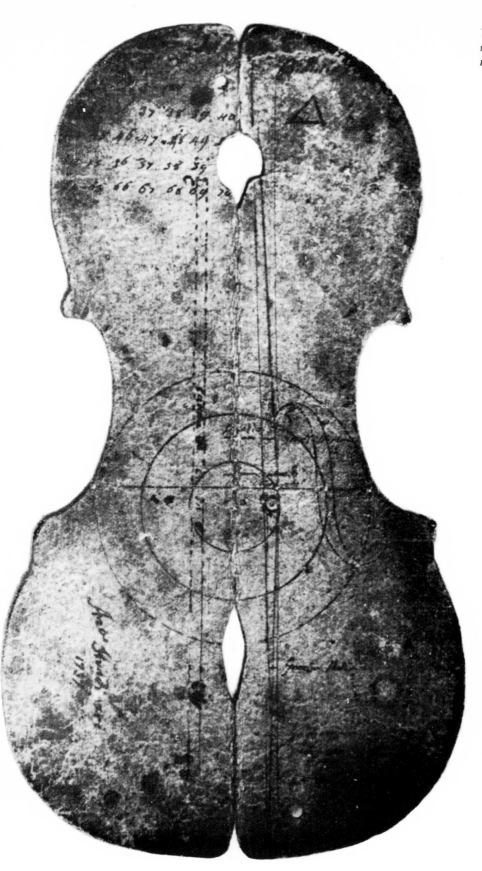

The pasteboard model attributed to Stradivari. It is more probably a reminiscence of the ancient technique of designing models.

several reasons, if only for the shape of the figures. Nor does one see very clearly why Stradivari should have made such a pasteboard model. At the age of eighty-nine, he would have had no need to set down what a long tradition had taught him. The authentic drawings by Stradivari published by Hill are known to us; they are studies of decorations for scrolls as Stradivari made them. Other drawings concern the shape of sound holes and show Stradivari's procedure for tracing them on the fronts. These authentic documents accord ill with the pasteboard attributed to this instrument maker. However that may be, this ancient pasteboard preserves the record of graphic methods, since lost, which permit the construction of the various parts of the violin's shape.

We also have a special calculation ruler which belonged to the instrument maker Facini, a monk who as an amateur made violins at Bologna about 1730–40. Formerly, this sort of ruler was in current use with mathematicians, and permitted them to determine the lengths of strings and arches, as well as tangents, secants, the elements of polygons, the golden number, etc. Facini's implement includes an arithmetical, geometrical, and cubic subdivision, as well as a graduation allowing a fixed angle to be given to two branches. The name *Facini* is engraved on it, accompanied by two little violins. This tool proves that some instrument makers used calculations in practising their art. It allowed the simple division of a length into a number of given parts, and the calculation of arcs of a circle in relation to the radius and the curvature, and it served as a protractor. Although some hypotheses put forward about this implement seem doubtful, it remains certain that instrument makers used mathematical or geometrical methods to set up their models.

ATTEMPTS TO RECONSTRUCT THE IDEAL SHAPE

In 1901 the Berlin instrument maker Carl Schulze published a book (128) entitled *Stradivaris Geheimnis* (*Stradivari's Secret*). Starting out from the definition of acoustic consonances in order to settle the proportions of the body of the violin, Schulze makes use of the following relations:

Absolute consonances : octave 1/2; twelfth 1/3; double octave 1/4;
Total consonances : fifth 2/3; fourth 3/4;
Medium consonances : major third 4/5; sixth 3/5;
Imperfect consonances : minor third 5/6; sixth 5/8.

Returning to the notions of Praetorius, he thinks that these various proportions must regulate the construction of bowed instruments in general. He analyses a classic model by Guarnieri, systematically seeking the above proportions in it. Considering only the interior structure of the violin as being important, Schulze takes as his modulus the length of 364.5 mm, which is the distance between the two end blocks at the top and bottom. He also analyses a model by Stradivari and gives a method of designing models of arches (arithmetical diminution of the rise between the middle of the arch and the edges). Schulze determines 'harmonic' proportions for certain points in the shape which

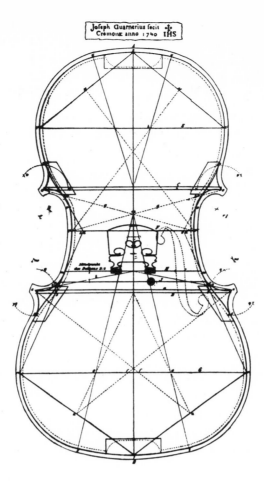

Joſeph Guarnerius fecit
Cremonæ anno 1740 IHS

Diagram by Schulze in which he reconstitutes the shape of the violin, relying purely on 'acoustical proportions' (1/2, 2/3, 4/5, etc.). The exterior shape depends on aesthetics; unlike Bagatella, Schulze joins his circles correctly.

depend on aesthetics alone. His measurements claim the accuracy of a tenth of a millimetre, which seems clearly exaggerated. I have also come across instruments which differ fairly widely from Schulze's designs, but are not inferior in sonority. Schulze thought that the violin's proportions were the essential point in the secret of the ancient Italian instrument makers. His diagrams fit in quite well with the shape of the classic violin, supporting our hypothesis that the ancient instrument makers used rules for drawing out their plans. Praetorius had earlier maintained that the subdivisions of the monochord were at the basis of the construction of instruments. But the acoustical quality of an instrument depends on other parameters, and 'Stradivari's secret' is certainly of another kind. The study by Schulze is not less interesting on account of the many coincidences which appear between the data he deduces and those of the beautiful classic models. He has the merit of insisting for the first time on the necessity of considering the interior structure of the violin significant only from the acoustical point of view.

In 1923, Adolf Beck, an instrument maker of Düsseldorf, published a small work (10), *Die proportionale Konstruktion der Geige* (*The Proportional Construction of the Violin*). He speaks of two laws of proportion which have been applied in constructing the violin:

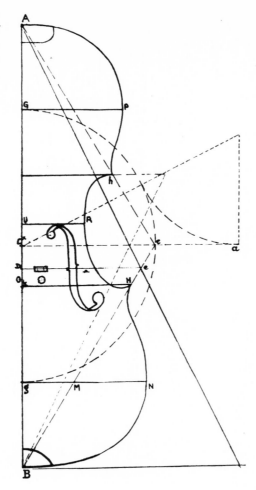

1 division in the ratio of the golden proportion (about 8/5);

2 division in the ratio 4/5, the acoustical proportion (the vibration numbers of the major third are in this ratio).

Contrary to Schulze, Beck starts from the full length of the table and settles his dimensions by constructing a series of segments connected among themselves by the golden number which he works out with the aid of the well known construction (a right triangle the sides of which are in the ratio of 1/2). Starting from a celebrated Stradivari model, Beck locates the 'aesthetic points' of the form of the violin. The acoustical point (the position of the bridge) is determined by the proportion 4/5: the front is divided into nine parts, and the bridge is placed on the fourth part counting from the bottom.

All these points are connected among themselves; variations are possible in the choice of centres. From the acoustical standpoint, Beck's thesis is rather naive, but the result of his diagrams is that the golden number appears with disquieting frequency in the shaping of the violin.

Max Möckel, a Berlin instrument maker, published in 1925 *Das Konstruktionsgeheimnis der alten italienischen Meister* (*The Construction Secret of the Ancient*

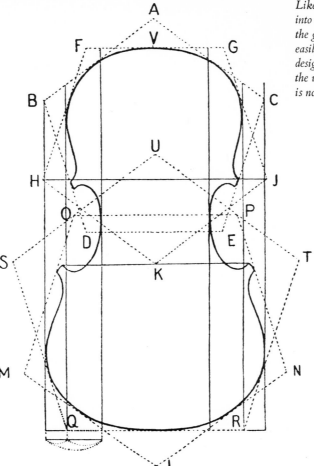

Italian Masters). This author endeavours to fit the shape of the violin into a system of pentagons, the elements of which are determined by the golden number. Möckel's idea is linked up with the geometrical speculations which Dürer had inherited from the neoplatonists. The diagram by Möckel fits some instruments quite well; others, no less classic, differ notably from it. For instance, Möckel makes the waist equal to one-half the width of the bottom, which – as I have verified on classic instruments – does not correspond to reality. The author calculates the thicknesses of the tables with the help of the golden number, which makes no sense from either the aesthetic or the acoustical point of view, nor does it agree with the achievements of master craftsmen of the classic period.

Dr. K. Steiner of Tübingen (134) has constructed a diagram of the violin, starting from the exterior length of the instrument's table. A golden series in terms of 356 mm, 220 mm, 136 mm, 84 mm, etc. is deduced from this 'modulus.' With the help of these dimensions, a trapezoid suited to the violin's shape is worked out. The accessory points are determined by a series of perpendicular lines to the longitudinal axis, and by three concentric circles 'which are found

The design by Steiner systematically uses the golden number. This procedure is complex, and the ancient instrument makers probably used simpler methods of design. But regardless how one analyses the shape of the violin, the golden number appears constantly. The concentric circles introduced by Steiner into his graph 'because they are found in an original drawing by Stradivari' add nothing to the sketch.

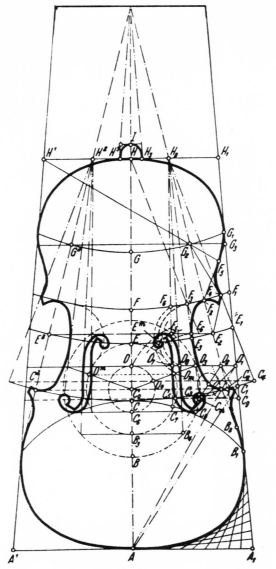

on an original model by Stradivari.' According to the author the design is 'surprisingly simple,' an assertion open to question. But it is curious all the same to notice that the golden number occurs in the violin no matter what the method by which one chooses to analyse its shape.

What should we think of these various attempts to reconstruct the shape by means of the golden number? The golden number can only regulate the visual aspect of the instrument's shape. Any attempt to attribute an acoustical value to such diagrams is indefensible. Now, many authors think they have thus discovered 'the secret' of the ancient instrument makers regarding the sonority of their instruments. The search for a precision which surpasses that which the maker of instruments can achieve, or which the eye can normally appreciate, is void of interest. If the golden number served in instrument making, its approxi-

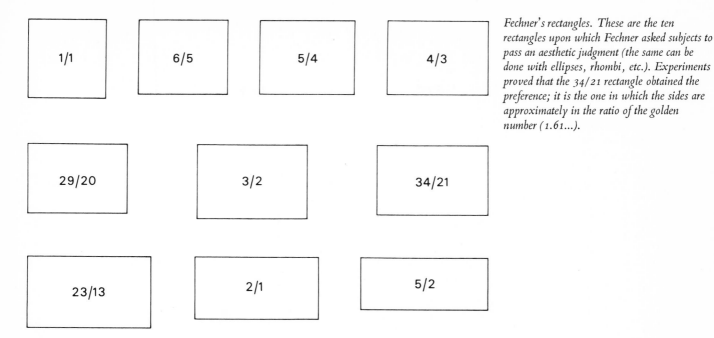

Inside the rectangles:

1/1   6/5   5/4   4/3

29/20   3/2   34/21

23/13   2/1   5/2

Fechner's rectangles. These are the ten rectangles upon which Fechner asked subjects to pass an aesthetic judgment (the same can be done with ellipses, rhombi, etc.). Experiments proved that the 34/21 rectangle obtained the preference; it is the one in which the sides are approximately in the ratio of the golden number (1.61...).

mations are sufficient. This is proved by the following test. Take a series of ten rectangles of different proportions: 1/1; 6/5; 5/4; 4/3; 29/30; 3/2; 34/21; 23/13; 2/1; 5/2. The majority of people asked to select the most 'beautiful' shape, chose the rectangle of which the two sides are in the relation of the golden section (34/21). This often repeated experiment of Fechner is significant. It is obvious that the difference between the exact value of the golden number – $\frac{1}{2}(1 + \sqrt{5})$ – and one of its approximations is aesthetically inappreciable. The values close to it are sufficient in aesthetics, because of the tolerance of the eye and the limitations of its power of discriminating shapes. It is the same in music, where the theoretical intervals of the scale are rendered with deviations, sometimes considerable ones (1/2 tone), without aesthetic enjoyment being diminished, even the contrary. Fluctuations form an integral part of musical style; to suppress them would mean monotony.

CONSTRUCTION OF A GOLDEN SERIES

Be that as it may, if instrument makers formerly used the golden number, it must have been in a simple form. Here are the methods for achieving the golden number which are of sufficient accuracy for instrument making.

Geometrical method: construction with ruler and compass   The designer starts from a right triangle ABY of which the sides BY and AB are respectively equal to 1 and 2; that is, the hypotenuse is $\sqrt{5}$. A simple drawing of two arcs of a circle from centres Y and A makes the division of the segment AB in the proportion of the golden number: AC = $\sqrt{5} - 1$, therefore AB/AC = 1.618, etc. By continuing the subdivision of the segments AC, AD, AE, a 'golden series' is obtained, two consecutive points of division being linked together by the golden number.

Method of designing a golden series. The small side BY *of the triangle is equal to half the large side* AB; *manipulations with compass and ruler divide* AB *into segments which are in the ratio of the golden number to one another. For example, the point* C *divides* AB *so that* AB/AC *equals* AC/CB; *this is the division in mean and extreme ratio, the very definition of the golden number. A shape with elements determined by a succession of this kind is 'beautiful,' in the measure in which, as Lalo said, 'the beautiful is the unity of multiplicity.'*

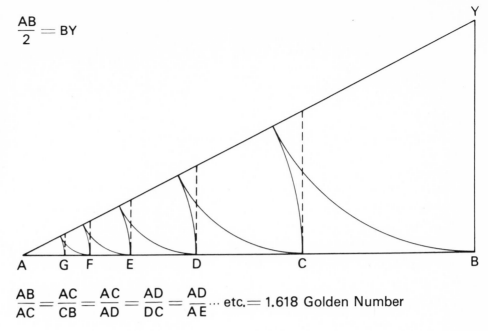

$$\frac{AB}{2} = BY$$

$$\frac{AB}{AC} = \frac{AC}{CB} = \frac{AC}{AD} = \frac{AD}{DC} = \frac{AD}{AE} \cdots etc. = 1.618 \text{ Golden Number}$$

The design of the star-shaped pentagon inscribed in a circle   A circle is drawn with two perpendicular diameters AZ and XY; one radius OY is divided into two equal parts; the manipulation indicated in the diagram (arcs of centre O′ and A) allows us to draw the regular convex pentagon and the star-shaped pentagon (in which we find the triangle ABC of the well known pentagram, the sides of which are in the proportion of the golden number). Further manipulations give a whole series of similar pentagons automatically connected to one another by the golden number. This construction is much more subtle than the previous one. On this subject the works of Matila Ghyka (37) may be consulted with interest.

The pentagram. A 'golden series' can be obtained very simply by drawing a regular pentagon. The design is made starting from O′ *in the middle of the radius* OY. *The arc* AM *subtends a chord* AM *equal to the side of the inscribed convex pentagon. From there one can easily draw a whole series of convex and star-shaped pentagons of which all the segments are connected with one another by the golden number. In fact, it can be demonstrated that the relation between the side of the star-shaped pentagon (*AB *for example) and the side of the corresponding convex pentagon (*BC) *is exactly equal to the golden number (1.618...). Such a diagram automatically gives a 'golden series,' the elements of which produce 'symphonic' co-modulated shapes in which everything is regulated by the golden number.*

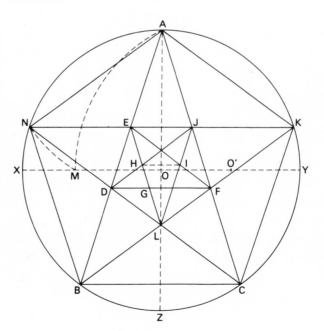

Golden Number
$$\frac{AB}{BC} = \frac{BC}{BD} = \frac{BD}{DE} = \frac{DE}{EJ} \text{ etc...}$$

Golden Series
AB - BC - DF - EJ - HI etc...

ABCD E F G

1 2 3 5 8 13

AB + BC = CD   BC + CD = DE   CD + DE = EF   DE + EF = FG

$$\frac{FG}{EF} = 1.625 = \text{Golden Number (within 1\%)}$$

Fibonacci's series. An extremely simple way of generating a golden series. Starting with adjoining segments one and two units in length, subsequent segments are drawn each equal to the total of the two segments which precede it; the ratio of two successive segments tends very rapidly towards the golden number. For example, the relation 8/5 = 1.6 is already a sufficient approximation in instrument making (in which deviations arising during construction are higher than 1/100 even among very competent makers). Mersenne explicitly gives this proportion for designing the shape of a lute.

The series of Fibonacci, in which the relation of two successive terms tends rapidly towards the value of the golden number, is also a method used. It is obtained by setting out from the first two whole numbers, each term being then defined as the sum of the two preceding ones; this gives 1, 2, 3, 5, 8, 13, 21, 34, 55, etc.; therefore 3/2 = 1.50; 5/3 = 1.67; 8/5 = 1.60; 13/8 = 1.62 ... By the sixth term we thus obtain the golden number to within a hundredth.

It is the first (or the last) method which was within the capacity of instrument makers, who were primarily artisans. In fact, Father Mersenne systematically used the relation 8/5 in designing the lute; moreover the ovolo used in the fourteenth century implicitly contained the golden number, as we have seen.

In instrument making, such factors as the inaccurate cutting out of moulds, and work on the unmounted instrument before the table is put in place, introduce errors far above 1/100; the practical value of 8/5 is therefore quite sufficient. The design starting from the triangle 1/2, however, presents no difficulty should a greater accuracy be judged necessary.

If a geometrical method is used in designing a directive diagram for the violin, it must satisfy three demands: it must have aesthetic sense, be simple, and leave the maker sufficient freedom.

$$\frac{AB}{AC} = \frac{AC}{CB} = \frac{DC}{AD} = 1.618 = \text{Golden Number} = \sim \frac{8}{5}$$

AB = 2 BY

We can see here how easily the principal elements of the violin can be worked out: length of the neck in relation to the body, place for the sound holes. The line for beginning the sound holes, perpendicular to AB at D, is indicated clearly on one of the few authentic drawings by Stradivari which have been preserved.

Father Mersenne's text is clear: 'The neck must have five parts, the belly eight.' The golden number is therefore present in the lute in the form of the relation 5/8 between the neck and the belly. The makers of lutes were also the first to construct violins, and there must exist a similarity between the design of the lute and that of the violin.

In fact, let us examine the length of the violin body, standardized long since at 35.5 cm. Father Mersenne's indications give $35.5 \times 5/8 = 22.2$ cm for the length of the violin neck, which coincides exactly with the original length of these necks: now they are about 23 cm, but we know that towards 1800, under the influence of the violinist Viotti, it became the fashion to lengthen the necks of the earlier violins systematically by a few millimetres.

To avoid all numerical calculation, one can use the following simple geometrical construction. Trace the total length AB = 57.7 cm; this segment is divided in mean and extreme ratio, giving the length of the neck and the place to start the sound holes.

DIVISION OF THE TABLE SURFACE

To assess the shape of a violin, it must be held in such a way that the eye is placed on the projection of a straight line in the middle of the table. The 'modulus' which allows the eye to comprehend the size of the instrument at once is the distance MC or MA between the middle of the table and the upper and lower edges. If the body measures 36 cm, the modulus will be $36/2 = 18$ cm.

Let us construct a golden series starting from this modulus by one of the methods studied above. Father Mersenne's method (based on 5/8) gives the following approximate series: 18; 11.25; 7.03; 4.39; 2.74; 1.71. But this method, although sufficient, accumulates errors, due to the approximation of the golden number to 8/5. The exact series gives: 18 cm; 11.12; 6.87; 4.25; 2.63; 1.63, so that the use of now the approximate method and now the exact method leads to the notable variations of shape, in millimetres, which we find in the classic models.

The series being chosen, let us draw the concentric circles having, respectively, the diameters given by the numbers of the series. All the points of two successive circles are, when considered from the centre, in the ratio of the golden number. We draw tangents to the circles at the points situated on the axis of symmetry and thus we get a whole network regulated by the golden number: ME/MF = MF/MH = MH/MK, etc.; we observe that all the noteworthy points of the shape of the classic violin coincide with those of the diagram.

This method is within the capacity of any craftsman; the mere knowledge of Father Mersenne's relation 8/5 suffices for the drawing of the design, thus settling the place of the corners, the narrowest point of the waist, the notches and the aperture for the sound holes, the place for the bridge, etc. The problem

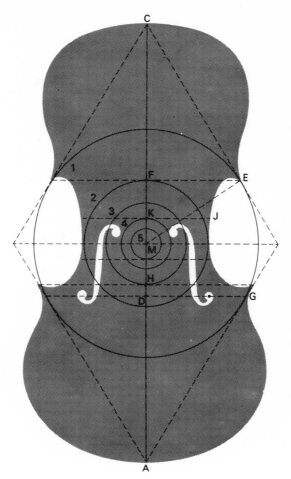

Golden diagram of the violin, worked out by E. Leipp. The shape of the violin can be defined without difficulty with the help of a diagram of merely a series of concentric circles. The starting point of the construction is the middle of the table M; the modulus is the distance MA (half the length); the theme is the golden number. We draw a series of concentric circles the diameters of which form a golden series obtained by any method. To estimate the shape of the violin is to compare mentally the distances from the significant points of this shape to the point M. If two points are situated on two successive circles, the relation of their respective distances to M is equal, by construction, to the golden number. We see that from these circles and a series of tangents perpendicular to the axis all the important points in the shape of the violin are obtained automatically. Such a design made up of circles and tangents was within the scope of instrument makers without special knowledge; these methods formed part of a technical inheritance the foundations of which go back to the tradition of Greek or Egyptian artists and architects.

of designing the violin consists, therefore, in first settling the 'strong point' of the shape (or M, the middle of AC) and then constructing round this point a diagram worked out with the help of the golden series or some similar one.

Tradition relates that the Gothic builders of the *Bauhütte* used to ask their fellow workers to find the initial point in a directive network, diagram, or shape. Their adage ran:

One point in the circle	*You know the point? Then all bodes well!*
Which is also in the square and triangle.	*You don't know it? All is in vain.*

The diagram of the violin is well in the tradition of the artists of the Renaissance period. In 1398 the architects unable to reach agreement over the completion of the Dome at Milan brought in the master architect from Paris, Jean Vignot, who uttered the famous phrase *Ars sine scientia nihil.* The science in question was primarily geometry as studied by many artists of the time; the case of Dürer is well known. Bartolomeo Facio, speaking of John van Eyck, said of him: 'Jean de Gaulois is considered the leading painter of our century, very well versed in the sciences, especially in geometry...' The examples could be multiplied.

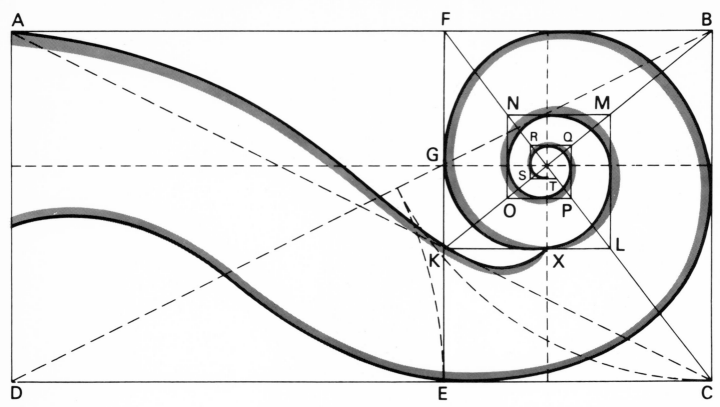

Design of the scroll of the violin. The method is always the same: a rectangle ABCD frames the head (BC/AB = 1/2); this rectangle permits the making of a golden series by one of the methods mentioned (AB/AF = AF/FB = golden number). We draw the diagonals FC and BK; we can show that FK/KE = EC/KL = FK/ML = ... = the golden number. Each coil is linked to the preceding and the following one by the golden number. The design is simple and automatic; the tangents to the coil have a meaning: they are the saw marks which the craftsman will make when he comes to outline the scroll of the head. To trace the head on the block of wood a model (a thin plate of wood or metal) is used which can be designed rationally. The chamfer, needed for solidity, is indicated by shading.

DESIGN OF THE HEAD

The golden number comes into the least details. We will take as example the design of the head and the scroll of the instrument. Present day instrument making is usually satisfied with copying the ancient models but it is obvious that in the beginning it was not so.

Analysis of the shape of the head of the classic violin is significant, and leads to the graph construction reproduced in the figure above. Let us draw the rectangle ABCD, the sides of which are in the relation 1 to 2. We cut the long side following the golden section (point F) so that the scroll strictly speaking (FB) will be in the ratio of the golden number with the head (AB). We then draw the diagonals FC and BK of the rectangle FBCE; we can show by similarity of the triangles that the golden number is found between the various segments: AB/AF = AF/BF = FE/FK = EC/KL = FK/ML = KL/MN, etc. = 1.618.

The eye follows this 'golden spiral' with a certain pleasure because at every point the diameters of two successive coils are automatically linked to one another by the golden proportion (e.g. FB/KL = KL/MN = MN/OP, etc.), which makes a kind of rhythm in space.

It will be noted that the scroll of the violin cannot be materially executed without making a chamfer the length of the spiral, for reasons of solidity. To satisfy aesthetics, this chamfer must be *inside* the spiral for the whole part ECBFKX, and *outside* at the theoretical line for the two turns of the final coils (framed by LMNOPQRST). This visual subtlety did not escape the great instrument makers. We have two drawings of scrolls by Stradivari which prove this. We see perfectly well at point x the crossing of the line of the chamfer with the spiral. It will be noticed that the central point of the scroll is clearly marked. We also see the drawing of the elementary lines of construction of the basic spiral, and we can observe that, designed with the aid of a model, it is very regular, whereas the line of the chamfer, drawn freehand, is irregular.

To sum up, it is the golden number which regulates the whole exterior shape of the violin. We can hardly doubt that the ancient instrument makers used it systematically; the coincidences are too numerous to be fortuitous. Methods of designing, however, were confined within the workshops, and these 'secrets' were lost, especially when the corporations were suppressed towards the end of the eighteenth century. It was an irreparable loss for instrument making, which has been condemned ever since to the sterile technique of copying, or to the formal extravagances which some modern innovations offer us.

The cabinet work of the violin is explained in many commercial textbooks: Alton (1), Millant (93), Roret (85), Tolbecque (137), Winckel (145), etc. Nevertheless, certain points deserve to be set down accurately. Before that, it is well to survey the various operations connected with the making of the violin. The technical terminology is illustrated by the figure on the next page.

PINE WOODS

This generic term includes various kinds with different characteristics. Practice has proved that the most valued variety is the *picea exelsa* or *pinus abies* (Linn.); it is the ordinary spruce, used in all ancient Italian and German instrument making. This wood has precious advantages: straight fibres, low density (roughly between 0.4 and 0.5), resistance to deformation. Sound travels quite rapidly in it (between 16,000 and 20,000 feet/second); the elastic modulus in the direction of the fibres is very high (1,100 to 1,500).

All spruce firs are not equally good for instrument making. Those which have grown in a flinty soil, in a temperate climate, and on slopes exposed to the sun at an altitude of 3,000–4,500 feet are usually selected. The growth rings (intervals between the fibres) are usually from 1 to 2 mm apart. The best woods come from Savoy, Switzerland, the Tyrol, Hungary, and Roumania.

The trunk is sawn up into pieces of 14 to 16 inches, which used to be split again with the hatchet in order to follow the grain of the wood well. The modern instrument-wood industry employs the saw, which gives rise to many inconveniences when it comes to the cabinet work. In the same length, considerable differences of quality can be observed from one piece of wood to another, according to whether the sample comes from near the root or near the top of the tree. These fluctuations in the elastic constants in the woods are one of the chief difficulties in instrument making, for the acoustic production depends not only on the shape of the instrument but on the physical parameters of the materials employed.

The craftsmen sort the woods by certain indications: colour, distance between fibres, brilliance of grain, etc. Unfortunately, there is no sure relation between the appearance and the physical properties. The most beautiful woods are not necessarily the best.

MAPLE WOOD

Several kinds are used concurrently; the plane maple (*acer platanoïdes*), and the sycamore maple (*pseudo-platanus*) are the principal ones. These woods come from Switzerland, the Tyrol, Bohemia, or Hungary. Their density is medium (0.6 to 0.8); sound travels definitely slower in them (10,000 to 13,000 feet/second) than in pine wood; and the elastic modulus is reduced by half.

Two important characteristics have determined the choice of this wood for the back. First, it looks very fine: the undulation of the fibres produce very beautiful plays of colour; second, its resistance to deformation is well known. The ancient turners used only maple poles as spindles for the treadles of their

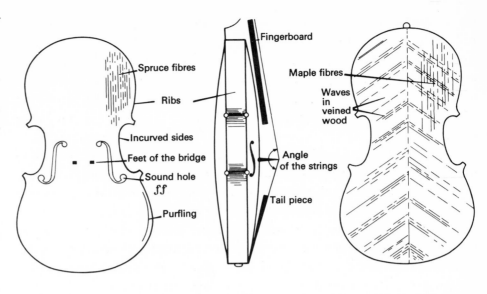

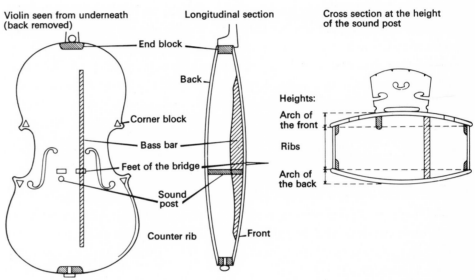

lathes, because this wood *never gives*. Like pine wood, maple varies a good deal from one sample to another. The ancient instrument makers selected on the spot the trees that suited their purpose. They thus obtained a certain homogeneity between the various pieces, allowing for gradual and empiric correction of their models. It is no longer so now, to the detriment of the quality of modern instrument making.

ACOUSTIC QUALITIES OF THE WOODS

Wood for instrument making is cut down in the winter, and cut into quarters which are stored in a dry, well-aired place for several years. Formerly, they were used only after at least five or six years of natural drying. Nowadays, these delays are disregarded, and attempts are made to dry the wood artificially by various methods, none of which have given really satisfactory results. Evaporation of the sap is not the only important feature; during the process of natural drying there is also an oxidation of gums, for example, which is lacking in forced drying processes. On the other hand, an exaggerated maturing of woods is not a good thing; in this case, they become brittle and lose their elastic qualities; certain instrument makers, who thought to obtain better results by using wood from very old, broken up furniture, have had experience of this.

The ancient makers understood the relation which exists between the qualities of their woods and the sound they gave under percussion. In 1636 Father Mersenne mentions a method certainly very old already in his time. A needle was stuck into a trunk several yards long, and it was made to vibrate by plucking it with the finger; another person, with his ear against the other end of the trunk, could clearly hear the note given by the needle. Nowadays, makers place the sample on three fingers, strike it with one finger, and judge the wood according to the note produced. Some use the Brinell method (estimating the depth of the imprint left by a marble pressed into the wood with a given force). Others measure the flexibility of test plugs of given dimensions in response to specific stresses.

All these methods are insufficient to evaluate the quality of wood for instrument making, which depends on its various physical properties. Now there are scientific methods of measuring the sensitive parameters of woods.

Density This can be measured easily. Given equal dimensions, it determines the weight of an instrument, and therefore its inertia, which in turn governs the transient response, that is, the duration of attack for a sound.

Muting coefficient This is determined by the nature of the inner structure of the material; it partially conditions the duration of extinction of sound once its active cause has stopped.

Speed of sound in the material This determines the clarity, the keenness of sound in the sample. It depends on the relation between the elastic modulus and the density of the material.

Rigidity can be tested by measuring torsional stress.

Resistance to deformation This matters a great deal. The violin undergoes considerable pressures with regard to both its dimensions and its bulk. Its sonorous qualities are modified by deformations.

Hygroscopicity Humidity modifies the properties of the woods, particularly when these are porous and contain hygroscopic salts.

Interesting studies have been published about the physical properties of woods for instrument making; the real difficulty no longer lies in measuring parameters but in interpreting them. The problem is further complicated by the fact that woods are anisotropic materials, the properties of which vary according to the direction of the cut. There are six possible ways to cut test plugs from a trunk; therefore, there are six muting coefficients, six elastic moduli, etc. On

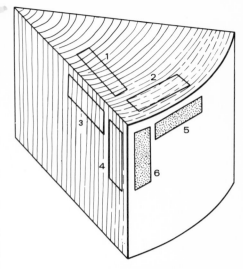

Anisotropy of wood. It is possible to cut plugs (small samples) from one piece of wood in six different ways. The more anisotropic the wood, the more unlike will be the properties of the gauges. In spruce the elastic modulus can vary by a factor of ten according to the direction.

the other hand, the fronts (tables) are drawn from the solid block; this chops the fibres in various ways. We can see how complex is the problem of materials.

The use of synthetic materials could simplify and facilitate the study of prototypes of instruments; unfortunately the shape and functioning of the violin are conceived according to the anisotropy of woods. The pure and simple copy of a violin in isotropic material, plexiglass or suchlike, is therefore senseless. It is not difficult to foresee the failure of such attempts.

PREPARATION OF WOODS

Cutting the wood radially Logs of pine or maple are cut in prism-shaped blocks. Each prism is re-split down the middle, and the two parts are beaten back like the cover of a book and joined by glue; this gives the roof-shaped board on which the model of the front or back is designed. This method achieves a certain symmetry of properties in relation to the join, but sometimes the front or back are taken from one piece, which does away with the join.

Another way is to saw the wood *in layers*, the log being then cut in parallel slabs. The drawback in this method is obvious; the properties of the various slabs vary from one to another, which does not happen in the radial cutting. That is why this manner of cutting the wood is not much employed.

Once the front and back are prepared, they are left untouched for a few days, since the pieces thus glued often warp. Finally, the basic material is planed in order to make it smooth, and the actual cabinet work begins.

Preparation of fronts. For the requirements of instrument making, a piece of wood can be cut either radially (1) or in layers (2). In the first case, the properties of the various prisms cut are about the same; in the second, they differ considerably from one piece to another. That is why radial cutting is preferred. The prism (3) is re-split from the top, and the two pieces are glued base to base (4); thus the slab used for the tables will have symmetrical properties in relation to the join.

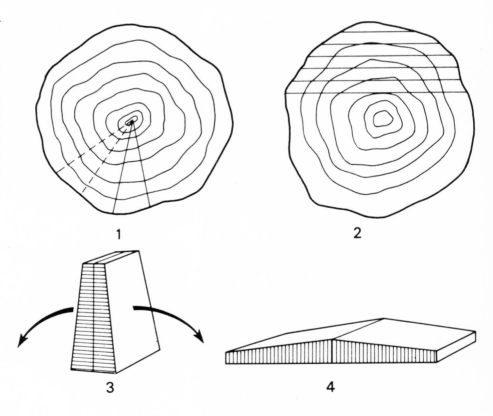

1

2

3

4

Textbooks on instrument making say little about methods of constructing the mould; makers have usually been content to copy classical models. A designing process probably conforming to the original techniques has already been outlined in the discussion of the origin of the violin. Here are the elements which permit us to reach an integral design of the shape of the mould.

On a very dry board about three-quarters of an inch thick we first draw the straight segment AB, of which the length, for the classical violin, is 32.4 cm (12¾ inches, a French royal foot); that is the *modulus*, the subdivisions of which will supply all the elements of the shape. This modulus is divided into three equal parts AX, XY, YB; in its turn, the segment XY is divided into three equal parts at the points C and Z.

A series of lines perpendicular to AB at these various points settles the horizontals of the violin's plan (DE, HI, FG). The perpendicular at x gives the line of the top corners, the perpendicular at z shows the place for the notch of the sound holes (and the bridge), the one passing through Y is tangent to the bottom of the sound holes.

The dimensions in width are obtained thus:

DE is equal to half the modulus;
FG is equal to five-fourths of DE;
HI is equal to one-third of the modulus.

This defines the geometry of the violin very simply; it suffices to unite the points correctly by arcs of circles from centres C, D′, E′, F′, G′, C′, C″. Several variants are possible (e.g. centres K, L).

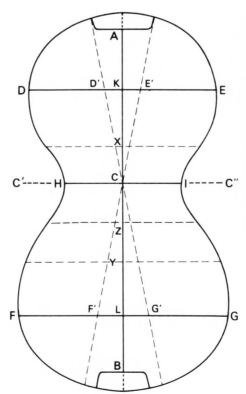

Design of a mould. The modulus is the interior length of the instrument, AB. This length is divided into three equal parts by the points X and Y. At K, the midpoint of AX, a straight line DE is drawn, equal in length to half the modulus AB; at L, the midpoint of BY, the straight line has a length FG = DE (5/4). The section XY is divided into three equal parts, and at C (1/3 of XY) a straight line is drawn HI = 1/3 of the modulus. The bridge will be placed at Z (YZ = 1/3 of XY). Thus the geometry of the mould is determined by the simple union of arcs of circles from centres C, E′, D′, F′, G′, C′, and C″. The latter two points are chosen to provide arcs that will connect smoothly with those drawn from D′, E′ and F′, G′.

This diagram presents the following interesting particularity:

$$\text{AZ} \times \text{DE} = \text{BZ} \times \text{FG}$$

In practice we verify that the point z is very near the centre of gravity, which is certainly not the result of chance; experiment, in fact, shows that the centre of gravity is the most important point from which to set the front vibrating.

Correction of the preceding plan The classical instruments show variations in the dimensions DE, FG, and especially HI, and a correlation has been observed between this width HI and the rise of the arch. In fact, the theoretical dimensions of the mould, previously defined, must be measured 'above' the tables. In these conditions it is evident that the width HI varies with the height of the arches; the mould must be corrected according to the arch. This is what the great instrument makers did: we know that Stradivari glued bands of cloth the length of the ƆC of his moulds, which allowed him to use the same mould with different rises of arch.

Finally, the contour of the mould being fixed, the board is cut out, making notches where the six cornerblocks (top and bottom and the four corners) will be provisionally glued.

The mounting of the mould is done by gluing in place the small blocks of wood (pine, lime, etc.) destined to form the frame of the instrument. The corners are cut with a penknife; according as they are made more or less pointed, the exterior aspect of the instrument is noticeably modified without altering the interior shape at all. A hot iron is then used to shape the ribs, thin boards of maple wood (1 mm) which have been previously soaked in water to prevent them from breaking. They are fashioned to the shape of the mould before their ends are glued to the corner blocks. To consolidate the whole and to increase the surface for gluing the tables to the ribs, the latter are doubled by counter-ribs in pine or lime wood. The mould is *mounted*; corner blocks, ribs, and counter ribs form the *foundations* of the instrument.

Correction of the mould. The arc AFA' is equal to the arc BF'B'. In the instruments made by masters of the art, we always find that the width depends on the height of the arches. This is particularly clear for the narrowest part of the instrument (the ƆC). The mould must therefore be corrected according to the height of the arch of the tables.

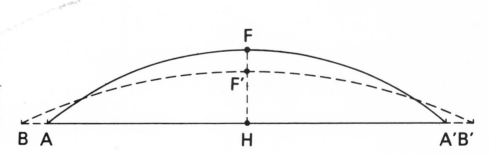

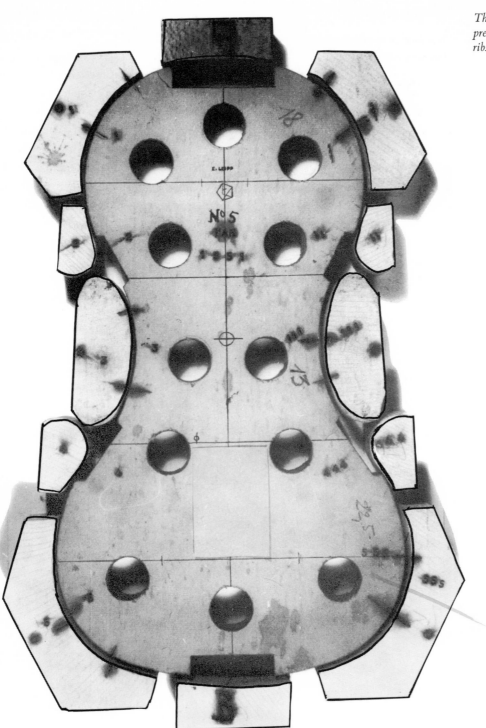

3 The Back, the Front, and the Neck

The *back* is taken from a solid block: the piece of maple, previously prepared, is first cut out with the help of a large gouge which is pushed by the body; then the shape of the back is roughly cut out with a turner's saw. Next, the arch is fashioned by using small planes with convex soles and iron teeth. Arch-shaped templates permit control while the work is in progress. Once the exterior arch has been roughly cut, it is smoothed with scrapers, simple blades of steel sharpened at a 90° or 45° angle, the edge turned back by means of a burnisher.

The back is then turned over and the inner surface is hollowed out, care being taken not to remove too much wood. The thicknesses are determined with calipers of various types, and taper from the middle (about 4 mm) towards the edge (about 2 mm). The manner of tapering the thickness varies with each maker, and obviously affects the instrument's acoustical qualities. The most celebrated makers seem to have been satisfied with approximations as to the thickness of backs and tops, and probably adjusted these from the outside when the instrument was finished.

A few millimetres from the edge a little channel is then hollowed out, and *purfling strips* are inlaid, two black and one white, intended to beautify the back and make the edges more solid. The edges are then made to fit the arch, properly so called, by means of a more or less pronounced groove (*ragreyure*), and the back is glued to the ribs. The mould is taken from the *box*, counter-ribs are glued on to the upper edge of the ribs, and the box is ready to receive the front.

The instrument maker's planes. To fashion the arches of the tables, instrument makers use small planes with a convex sole, the iron of which has lines running lengthwise to form teeth, so that woods of irregular structure can be worked on without causing splinters. The smallest of these planes is called a noisette *in French; the length of its sole is 28 mm.*

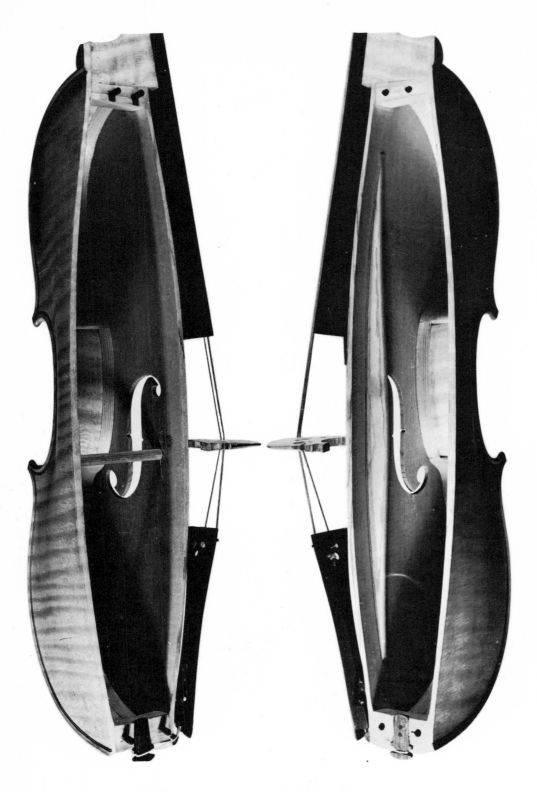

Work on the front is the same as that on the back in every way, but the table is often made with uniform thickness. The sound holes are traced with the aid of exact models in wood or metal, and then cut out with a thin-bladed pen-knife.

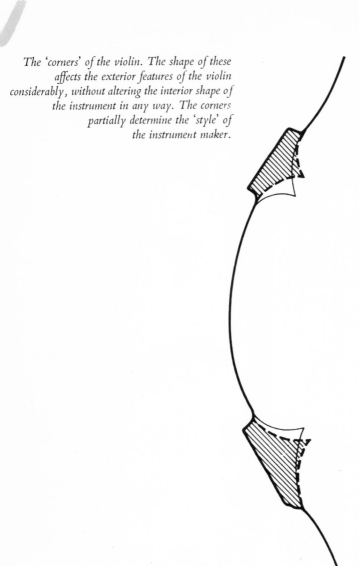

The 'corners' of the violin. The shape of these affects the exterior features of the violin considerably, without altering the interior shape of the instrument in any way. The corners partially determine the 'style' of the instrument maker.

The bass bar is then glued 15 mm from the longitudinal axis and under the left foot of the bridge. It is a straight piece of pine wood, from 4 to 5 mm thick, the width of which decreases from the middle (about 15 mm) to the ends, and the length of which (about 27 mm or 10½ inches) varies according to the maker. The bass bar is customarily *forced*: it is given a bend that is greater than the arch of the front and pressed forcibly against the front with a pinch bar. The bass bar has a major effect on the sonority of the instrument, as Father Mersenne pointed out. Too strong a bass bar increases the inertia of the top and lessens the degree of freedom of the left foot, which governs the low notes. It is an important point in the instrument makers' art, and they make a great mystery about it. We shall see what it actually is when we speak of acoustics.

The front being finished, it is glued to the ribs. Now the violin's resonating box is finished. All that remains is to make and adjust the neck.

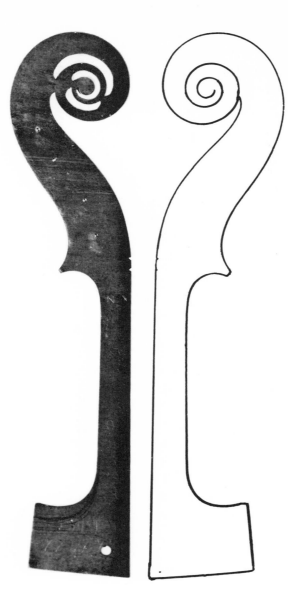

The *neck* is taken from a block of maple wood on which the shapes of the handle and of the scroll have been traced with an exact model. First the *peg box* is fashioned, then the scroll is carved with gouges of different sizes. The *end piece* which will be joined to the instrument's upper block is cut dovetail in order to give all the necessary solidity to the gluing of the neck. Before the neck is finally fixed, the fingerboard, a thin piece of ebony, is lightly glued to it. The fingerboard must rise sufficiently above the table to allow the instrument to be played easily. The neck being set in and glued into position, the fingerboard is replaced by a small provisional piece of wood, which will be less in the way during varnishing.

Next, the whole instrument is cleaned, scraped, and rubbed with sandpaper or a supple scraper; it is then wiped over with a damp sponge and everything is ready for the important operation of varnishing.

4 The Shape of the Arches and the Tilting of the Neck

The violin is made of thin boards which undergo considerable pressure; in fact, the total tension of the four strings is something like 20 kg (44 lb). Now resistance to deformation depends on two factors: the choice of materials, which has already been discussed, and the division of the forces present, which is related to the shape of the instrument and especially to that of the arches.

The ancient instrument makers knew the advantages of the ovolo, which they employed from the fourteenth century to make the primitive lute. They had observed that the ovolo offers remarkable resistance to deformation, permitting the bulk of the instrument to be reduced to the minimum, a favourable condition for sonority. But in instruments demanding incurved sides to allow for the passage of the bow, the ovolo shape is no longer suitable. So the violin makers employed another shape well known to Renaissance architects, possessing the same qualities as the ovolo and an analogous simplicity of construction: the ellipse.[1] In fact, if we examine the shape of the mould we discover two ellipses, the first with foci at D' and E'; the second with foci at F' and G'.

The same necessity, maximum resistance and minimum of bulk, reappears in the shaping of the arches. I have studied and analysed the shape of many front and back arches of ancient classic instruments, and have observed that this shape was statistically close to the mathematical curve called the *catenary*. It is curious to notice that the Italians call the violin's bass bar *catena*, that is, chain; this name is easily explained if the arch against which the bass bar rests has itself the shape of a catenary: i.e. the shape taken naturally by a heavy thread or small chain with fine links when held hung up by the ends. The properties of this curve have long been empirically known; if Galileo still considered it a parabola, Bernoulli found its true mathematical formula in 1691. For instrument making this shape offers considerable advantages.

It can be demonstrated that, when the curve is slight, the force is the same on each link of a chain. So if we use the catenary shape when constructing the arches of the violin, the strain resulting from the tension of the strings is shared equally among all points of the front, which, owing to this fact, is less easily deformed.

Besides that, the catenary arch is easy to make. It suffices to hang up a jewel-metal chain between two nails to determine the rise (height of the arch) and to reproduce on paper or by photography the shape achieved. By pasting the photograph onto a board and cutting it out, we obtain an exact *model* of the arch of the violin.

Having constructed a series of violins with catenary arches, I have noticed that after years of use these instruments become much less deformed than others made differently. Therefore the very special shape of the violin is perfectly rational. It is the result of the imperious need to obtain maximum resistance to deformation combined with minimum bulk, conditions which are indispensable for the quality of sound and the life of the instrument.

[1] Geometrically, the shape of the violin can be reduced to two ellipses, united by two arcs of a circle.

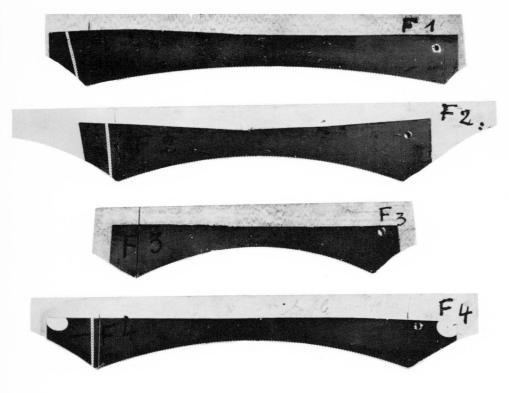

The tilting of the neck is thus described in the *Manuel du luthier* (*Instrument Maker's Handbook*) by Roret:

A ruler is placed on the middle of the fingerboard, and a set-square on the place where the bridge is to go; the point fixed by the extension of the fingerboard and the side of the set square must be placed $12\frac{1}{4}$ lines above the table. This elevation of $12\frac{1}{4}$ lines is the exact rule for the tilting.

That is certainly not the procedure of the classic instrument makers, whose technique, as we have seen several times, always justified itself.

Let us examine the longitudinal section of a violin. The tension T of the strings determines a system of forces which can be set down schematically as follows:

1 the force f_1, applied to the top of the bridge, is perpendicular to the table and tends to drive it inwards;
2 the tension of the strings at the point of attachment A can be analysed into a force f_2, tending to raise the neck (and lower the fingerboard towards the table), and another force f_3 directed towards the table along the neck AB.

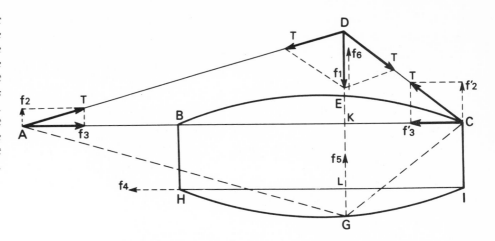

The force f_2 is applied to the system of levers ABH; the back is stretched by the force f_4, variable with the relation $\mathrm{AB/BH}$. The back therefore tends to flatten, causing a thrust upwards, f_5, communicated to the table by the sound post EG. Also, the opposing forces f_3 and f'_3 press on the table at both ends, and cause by lateral flexion a thrust f_6, applied at E (foot of the bridge) and directed upwards.

When the action f_1 and the reaction $f_5 + f_6$ are equal, the system has attained equilibrium; it is the most favourable condition for setting the table vibrating with minimum force. The classical makers achieved this result by always arranging the disposition so that the point A (nut of the neck) was very carefully placed on the extension of the table (BC).

Let us draw the quadrilateral ADCG. In classic models this quadrilateral is always regular: the triangle ADC equals the triangle AGC. Thus, the forces resulting from the tension of the strings are applied, on the one hand, to the material system ABC (neck + front), and on the other, to the system DEG (bridge + sound post). The length of the sound post EG is equal to the total $\mathrm{EK} + \mathrm{KL} + \mathrm{LG}$ (arch of the front + ribs + arch of the back). The equality of the triangles is then achieved when $\mathrm{DE} + \mathrm{EK} = \mathrm{KL} + \mathrm{LG}$, or *height of bridge + height of arch of the front = height of the ribs + height of the arch of the back.*

To confirm our notion, let us take the example of the violoncello. It has always been asked why the bridge of this instrument was so high in proportion to the length of the body. The rule laid down above supplies the answer; since for acoustical reasons the ribs of the violoncello are very high (4 inches on the average) the bridge will also measure 4 inches if the arches of front and back are the same.

To sum up, the tilting of the neck is a determining parameter in instrument making. Craftsmen make it a great mystery, whereas it is a simple problem of angles, though delicate to carry out in practice. In any case it is evident that the tilting of the neck must be adapted in each instrument to the dimensions of the ribs and the arches. It cannot, as textbooks on the craft maintain, be given a fixed numerical value for all instruments.

Stradivari's secret is the varnish   This statement, repeated for two hundred and fifty years, rests on no proof. In reality, in instrument making, varnish plays a triple role. The instrument is made with white woods to which varnish gives the aspect of precious wood; with this end in view, the colours of the varnishes vary traditionally from yellow to brown, passing through shades of red. Second, because it is intended for constant handling, the violin would soon collect stains if it were not covered with varnish. Lastly, varnish plays an acoustical role because it can modify the natural qualities of the wood (density, elasticity, damping) and therefore the sound of the instrument. The ancient Italian makers were past masters in the art of varnishing musical instruments. What do we know for certain about their varnishes and their technique?

HISTORY OF VARNISHES

Legend to the contrary, no one has ever found a written recipe for the varnish used by the ancient Italian makers. Some documents show that no particular importance was attached to the varnish. A letter addressed to the Duke of Ferrara in 1526 tells us that the celebrated lute maker Maler left the preparation of varnishes to his apprentices, and that he made use of two sorts of varnish. Another letter from a contemporary of Stradivari shows that this maker was famous for his design, his inlaid work, but not for his varnish, of which no special mention is made.

We know that these varnishes took a long time to dry, because Stradivari himself, in one of the rare authentic letters from him which we possess, offers excuses to a client for being unable to finish repairs to an instrument in time, because the part revarnished had taken a long time to dry. A letter from Galileo confirms that the drying of the varnishes was a source of annoyance to instrument makers, and states elsewhere that an instrument could not be brought to perfection 'without the strong heat of the sun.' This is about all we learn from the authentic documents.

Some, such as Greilsamer, have put forward the hypothesis that the Italian instrument makers themselves did not know the recipe for the varnish they employed and that a druggist supplied it.

I have only found one precise indication of the composition of varnish for musical instruments, in a document quoted by Ziloty (156). It is a manuscript left us by the doctor of Mayerne who was keenly interested in the technical problems of painting and varnishing. In it we read of a Florentine painter who added to the white he used 'a drop of amber varnish obtained from Venice, with which they varnish lutes, and the varnish, although red, does not spoil the white.' We know, therefore, that in 1630 a red 'amber varnish' was used for lutes. Many documents of that period tell us, however, that the 'amber varnish' was not made from amber (since craftsmen did not then know how to dissolve it), that it was a varnish of amber colour, made with linseed oil and colophony (Greek pitch).

I have carefully studied the only known systematic treatise on varnish which dates from Stradivari's time, the *Traité des vernis*, published in Rome in 1720 by Father Filippo Bonanni, and translated into French in 1723 (18). This treatise contains a mass of technical information and recipes for all sorts of things, without making any reference to varnish for violins or musical instruments. It is only in 1773 that we find recipes for varnishing violins (*L'Art du peintre doreur et vernisseur* by Watin, 143); but the varnishes spoken of in this work have nothing in common with those employed by the ancient Italian instrument makers. They are classical spirit varnishes with a basis of sandarac, gum-lac, mastic, or copal. The original recipes used by the Italian makers were lost towards the end of the eighteenth century, and there appears to be no possibility of finding them.

After that, a great number of research workers devoted their energies to recovering the lost secret. The publications, often interesting, by Fry (35), Mailand (82), Greilsamer (40), etc., prove that the secret was not found. The reasons for this failure are many; the researchers had insufficient methods and apparatus for scientific work, and they relied on ancient documents in attempts to reconstitute the recipes. This method is very precarious; the ancient documents mention numerous products once in current use but long since abandoned. The names of gums and resins have altered with time. Products often bore the name of the settlements where Europeans had bought them, and these names changed with the modification of sea routes. Venice was the great import centre for Eastern products. When the Turks closed the eastern Mediterranean to Venetian ships, resins were imported via Genoa from North or West Africa. The cutting of the Suez Canal also led to many changes. Besides that, the same name often designated products which were entirely different, and interpretation of the ancient documents becomes extremely uncertain from this very fact. For example, in 1740 Lémery says, in speaking of benzoin: 'They say that it comes from Arabia and is found in the mountain where incense grows, that it is what the ancients called myrrh.' Even in 1911, Cordemoy says, in his treatise *Les Plantes à gommes et à résines*, that there are three kinds of myrrh, but that 'the real myrrh has a more complex, and in part doubtful, origin.' However that may be, from the nineteenth century, instrument makers, unable to reproduce the beauty of the ancient varnishes, came rapidly to attribute extraordinary virtues to them. It was thought that with the Cremona varnish, beauty both of appearance and of sound had been lost; it was then that the most extravagant legends sprang up which have come down to our own times.

PHYSICAL PROPERTIES OF THE ANCIENT VARNISHES

The beautiful Italian varnishes of the seventeenth and eighteenth centuries possessed remarkable features:

  great transparency and highly saturated coloration;
  a *moist*-appearing surface;
  an under-varnish, or sizing, generally yellow in colour, and different from the top-varnish;

dichroism: under the influence of light from a given direction, the maple wood back shows alternate bands of red or brown and yellow, according to the grain of the maple; by gradually changing the orientation of the light, the same undulation can be made to appear yellow and red successively. This shimmering is highly esteemed, and most modern varnishes reproduce it only very faintly;

solubility of the coloured top-varnish in spirits;

flexibility of the varnishes; the fingernail easily makes an impression and the varnish does not *flour* when scratched.

Several authors have pointed out that when fingers are pressed on this varnish for a long time, they leave marks. This indicates either a varnish of weak fusion, or a varnish partially soluble in water, or an unskilful cleaning.

But how can these features explain the acoustical properties and visual properties attributed to the ancient instrument makers' varnishes?

VARNISH AND THE SONORITY OF THE VIOLIN

Experience shows that the violin's sound alters perceptibly after varnishing; therefore the process must modify one or several physical properties of the instrument.

Density   The penetration of products into the tables increases the density of the wood. This usually varies from 0.40 to 0.60 for pine wood, and from 0.55 to 0.85 for maple. The resins currently used in instrument varnish have a density of from 1.05 to about 1.5 (colophony 1.07 to 1.08; amber 1.08; copal 1.04 to 1.06; sandarac 1.08 to 1.09; gum-lac 1.15, etc.). The density of the resins is therefore a little higher than that of the woods. The increase in the weight of a table of about 3 ounces, once it is varnished, is of the order of a few drams. The increase of density is therefore negligible, except in the case of penetrating varnishes, for example varnishes of linseed oil applied without sizing. Therefore the density of resins cannot notably modify the sound of the instrument.

Elasticity   The chapter on acoustics will show how elasticity is connected with the spectrum, that is, with the quality of the sound. Practice demonstrates that a top-varnish causes only insignificant alterations in the sound. It is quite otherwise with penetrating varnishes. In this case, the tender parts of the wood (summer wood) absorb oil and resin voraciously. During the drying – which can take a very long time – the summer wood hardens gradually, and a *homogenization* of the pine wood takes place: in the table the elasticity of transverse flexion draws closer to the longitudinal elasticity, and under these conditions the sound of the instrument alters with time. But my own observations on fragments of ancient instruments have shown that the penetration of the varnishes formerly used by instrument makers was slight, something like a tenth of a millimetre, and therefore could not greatly modify the elasticity of the woods, nor, consequently, the sound emitted by the violin.

Rigidity Instrument makers empirically estimate the rigidity of tables by holding them at both ends and subjecting them to torsion tests. Experience in varnishing shows that the torsional rigidity of a table varies very little with the light varnishes such as the ancient makers used.

Damping capacity If the table of the violin is struck, the vibration dies away gradually. The damping speed depends on many parameters; the internal friction of the materials, combined with their molecular structure, plays an important part. Now, varnishing can certainly modify the damping capacity of the tables. Experience proves that a good damping capacity is indispensable for musical instruments, but if it is too great the instrument becomes dull; the ancient Italian makers seem to have reached a summit in this matter. At the beginning of this century, it was thought that the secret had been found in using thick, more or less penetrating varnishes. Since linseed oil hardens gradually, the best damping capacity is reached at a certain stage in the drying process, but after that stage the instrument deteriorates, which did not happen with celebrated classical instruments. The ancient makers must have used products unaffected by time.

Having done some research in this matter, I have found that there are some resins used in ancient pharmacopoeia which become plastic at body temperature (gum ammoniac, *assa foetida*, etc.) and which can be used in the preparation of varnishes. But I have observed that after about ten years these varnishes lose their suppleness, which depends on the presence of vegetable essences. Now these essences partially evaporate and solidify more or less rapidly. If the varnishes of the ancient instrument makers have remained supple after several hundred years, their pliancy cannot be attributed to this type of resin. Nor can there be a question of varnishes made with oily essences, which were praised once and which I have tried (essence of lavender, rosemary, etc.). Experience proves that all these varnishes become as dry and floury in a few years' time as the ordinary spirit varnishes.

S. Arakelian (2), an instrument maker in Teheran, thinks that the foundation of the Italian makers' varnish was myrrh. Historically that is not impossible; one notes its use in many pharmaceutic recipes (Lémery, *Nouveau Recueil des plus beaux secrets de médecine*, 1740). I have made varnish with a basis of myrrh, but in a few years it hardened like all varnishes made with essences, and for the same reason: myrrh must owe its supple quality to an essential oil which does not retain its properties with time. Arakelian stated later that this varnish on a myrrh basis must be prepared with a little spirit, because myrrh contains a certain amount of gum, soluble in water, which makes the varnish liable to receive fingerprints if pressed for a long time. Father Bonanni (18) certainly mentions myrrh in his *Traité des vernis*, but gives no recipe containing this ingredient which Watin (143) expressly says should be avoided.

Therefore neither linseed oil nor any other siccative oils nor vegetable essences can give the most permanent damping properties to the tables. The secret of the supple Italian varnishes lies elsewhere.

I have made use of waxy products, some of which are very stable. Among these, *propolis* was in current use in the sixteenth and seventeenth centuries, and I have verified that varnishes containing it remain supple for a very long time. *Propolis* is a waxy substance collected by bees to caulk badly joined hives. The presence of pollen detected under the microscope in some ancient varnishes could confirm the hypothesis that *propolis* was used in making them.

VISUAL PARTICULARITIES OF THE ANCIENT VARNISHES

Brilliancy   The paste of the old Italian varnishes seems to be a peculiarly shining product. It is known that this quality is connected with the index of refraction of the constituent materials. A ray of light passing from a slightly refracting medium into a highly refracting one will break up. In this case, the angle of incidence i is greater than the angle of refraction r, and only one portion of the light penetrates into the second medium, the other being reflected on the surface (R_1). The proportion of light reflected by the surface depends on the difference of the indices of refraction of the two media. The higher the index of refraction in a varnish, the more light is reflected on the surface. Thus, linseed oil has an index of refraction of 1.485 and colophony 1.543. The index of refraction in a spirit varnish based on colophony will be 1.543 after evaporation of the solvent, and a varnish of colophony and linseed oil will necessarily have a weaker one. Therefore, varnish with pure colophony will be brighter than a varnish with oil and colophony, but less resistant than the latter. This has been proved in practice.

Chemical analysis of natural resins is very delicate and they are not well understood. There is no question of a chemical analysis of a varnish, especially if it is very old, oxidized, and modified by revarnishings and the application of preservative products of all kinds. The index of refraction, on the contrary, can supply us with objective information on the brilliancy of a varnish.

Transparency   In spite of their strong colour, the ancient Italian varnishes have a remarkable transparency. The care that the ancient craftsmen and artists took in selecting and sorting their gums and other ingredients certainly had something to do with this. We learn from physics that a coloured varnish is all the more transparent, since the index of refraction in the colouring matter is closer to that of the resins which make up the varnish. Resins coloured naturally or resinous colouring matter (dragon's blood, gamboge, etc.) usually supply this condition. These products were once used to effect, as actual documents prove. Therefore it is the indices of refraction which determine the brilliance and the transparency of a varnish. This fact has not been sufficiently brought out.

Scintillation   The classical varnishes offer a further peculiarity. Under the microscope and under directed light, we observe myriad bright dots that glisten as the direction of the light changes. When a ray of light passes from a refracting medium into a less refracting one, we notice that at a given angle of incidence no light passes through the surface between the two media; this is known as

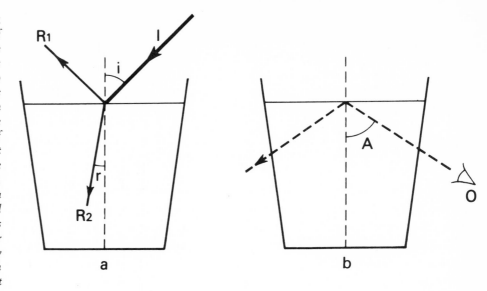

total internal reflection. The experiment is easily made by looking at the lower surface of a glass of water; at a given angle *A*, the surface of water-air contact is like a silvery mirror. The critical angle at which this total reflection is produced is smaller as the difference between the respective indices of the media is greater. It is precisely this total reflection of light on the small surfaces of wood, lying at various angles, that produces these very bright scintillations. The scintillations therefore pose a problem of differences of refractive index.

In these conditions, it is well to give a little information about sizing. All craftsmen know that it is impossible to varnish a violin properly with a coloured varnish unless the wood is first sized to restrict its capillarity. In fact, the irregularity of the absorption coefficient of the table surfaces causes unaesthetic stains. The problem of sizing is this: we must use a product that restricts the capillarity of the wood and at the same time possesses the lowest possible index of refraction in relation to that of the varnish employed. The final appearance of the varnished surface depends therefore not only on the recipe of the varnish, but on the properties of the subjacent layers, that is, the sizing. This explains the failure of those who endeavour to discover the formula of *Cremona varnish* only; the formula alone is not enough, because the authentic Cremona varnish, applied to a surface with too high a refractive index, cannot give the visual result observed on ancient instruments. Tolbecque made this experiment by applying to new wood the authentic Cremona varnish collected from cut fragments of old instruments. A letter from Jacopo de li Tibaldi to the Duke of Ferrara, written in 1526, tells us that instrument makers used two varnishes; oral tradition also declares that makers at Cremona employed two varnishes of different kinds, one on top of the other. All these statements agree; the problem of the index of refraction is all-important, and explains the appearance of the ancient instrument varnishes.

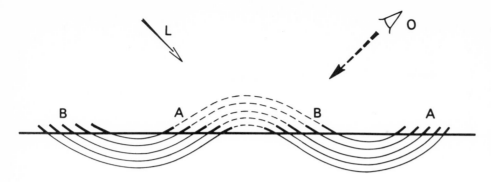

Polarization of light   When we look at beautiful old Italian instruments in a diffused light, the surface of the back looks a fairly uniform yellow or orange. But if we direct a beam of light along the back in a given direction, we notice bright colours – for example, red-yellow alternating in the grain. This is a matter of light polarization. Many observations and experiments have shown that the effects of polarization were known to the ancient Italian instrument makers.

Let us consider the longitudinal section of the back of a violin. Maple fibres are not straight but undulating. Now, these fibres are cut smooth when the surface of the back is levelled by planes and scrapers. But since these tools never cut perfectly clean, the wood's surface presents an aspect more or less like velvet; in the grain we see hairs pointing in opposite directions, as in A and B, and these hairs determine a polarization of light. According to the direction of the light and the position of the eye, zone B, in which there are total reflections, will appear very light, while zone A will be dark and saturated with colour. After many experiments the phenomenon is very obvious, and the direction in which the wood is planed bears an important part. The hairs are flattened in one direction or the other, as when we make polarizing screens. When we use fine sandpaper on the wood's surface, the effect disappears almost entirely. The invention of sandpaper made the surfacing of the tables easier, but was an essential cause of the decadence of beautiful violin varnishes.

To sum up, the problems of varnishing can be solved thanks to a scientific approach; apparatus and methods are to hand, and the secret of the ancient varnishes can be discovered. This applies to the whole technique of violin manufacture; science is now able to solve various problems raised by instrument making. Unfortunately, too many instrument makers are not yet convinced of this and reject with indignation any intrusion of science into their art. There is no doubt that this spirit is one of the principal causes of the stagnation in instrument making. One day it will have to be admitted that art is nothing without science.

ACOUSTICS IV

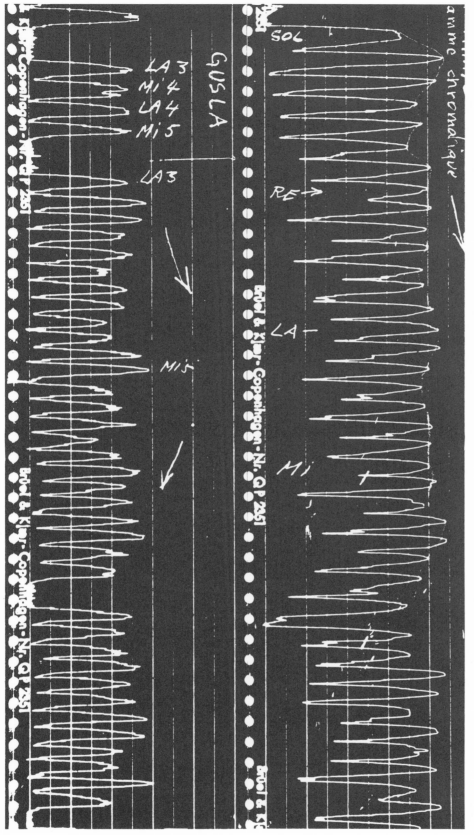

A musical instrument is a machine to produce sounds destined to be integrated by the human brain; it is only a link in the chain of communication of musical messages and makes no sense except in relation to the whole of this chain. In the simplest case, that of direct hearing, this chain begins in the composer's brain and ends in that of the listener. In it we observe:

objective elements: physical parameters and factors which can be recorded and measured;

subjective or psycho-physiological elements: memory, sensations, etc. introduced by the intervention, thrice repeated, of the ear and the human brain, the co-ordinates of which are essentially fluctuating and ill-defined.

The problem of the recording and measurement of objective phenomena can now be considered as solved, but the interpretation of the results obtained presents great difficulties. In fact, the perception of the signal radiated by an instrument depends not only on the anatomy and physiology of the ear, which vary with the individual and his age, but also on the mechanism of integration by the brain, which involves factors from the world outside: education, custom, traditions, etc.

The problems raised by telecommunications and the recording of music have advanced research in the field of audition. Research has succeeded in distinguishing the statistical peculiarities of the functioning of the ear and the brain, many of which have also been empirically known and exploited by musicians and instrument makers since ancient times.

1 A Few Facts in Psycho-physiology

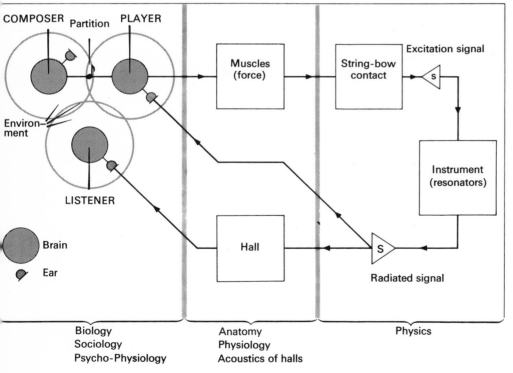

The chain of communication of the musical message. Even in the simple case of direct audition it is extremely complex. The presence of the human brain and ear with their reciprocal reactions introduces mobile and fluctuating psychological factors into the auditory cycle. The objective musical signal only has meaning, therefore, in relation to the psycho-physiology of audition. It must be interpreted; that is the delicate point of musical acoustics.

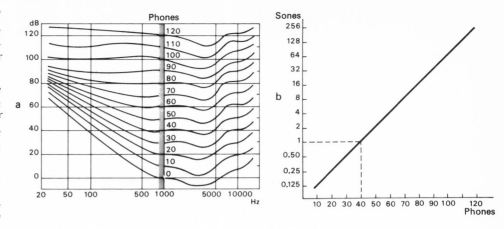

THE NON-LINEARITY OF THE EAR

The sensibility of the ear varies with frequency, as the isotonic curves of Fletcher and Munson demonstrate. These variations are all the more important as the volume of the signal grows weaker. The maximum sensibility of the ear is between 1,000 Hz (c5) and 3,000 Hz (g6); on either side of this range, sensitivity diminishes. It is therefore evident that to obtain identical sensations of volume with instruments of different tessitura, the scale of the instruments must increase according as their average tessitura departs further from the sensitive zone of the ear.[1] Since the ear's curve of sensibility does not follow a simple law, it is the same for the dimensional relations between instruments of different tessitura. For example, the violin has a body length of 14 inches; the viola, tuned a fifth lower, is not at all in the ratio 3/2 with the violin; it measures about 16 inches instead of 21. Therefore, the dimensions of instruments are governed by psycho-physiological laws also, and not by physical laws alone.

Moreover, the preceding isotonic curves hold good only for sinusoidal sounds; they do not hold for musical sounds composed of variable series of elementary frequencies (harmonics and partials). Consequently, the pitch of a musical sound is linked with its spectrum, that is, with its timbre. It is the distribution of the energy within the spectrum in relation to the sensitive zone of the ear which determines the subjective volume of a sound.

Besides that, it is known that the nerve cells respond to the law of 'all or nothing'; they function from a certain threshold of excitation, but the sensation remains unchanged if this threshold is passed, even to a considerable degree. All the energy spent on augmenting the amplitude of a harmonic above the threshold will therefore be wasted auditively, and an augmentation of the sensation of intensity could only flow from an increase of the *number* of nerve cells excited. If this is so, the problem arises at what level of the auditive apparatus the increase takes place. Is it in the internal ear (basilar membrane) or in the

[1] We call *sensitive zone of the ear* that part of the area of audibility included between 500 and 5000 Hz, where the density of information is the greatest.

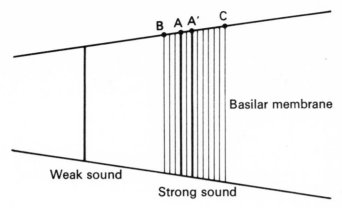

B A A' C

Basilar membrane

Weak sound

Strong sound

Variation of pitch with volume. According to the partisans of the theory of the localization of pitch in the basilar membrane, the weak sound would only excite a narrow strip on the basilar membrane; the sound is 'pure' and its pitch clearly defined. If the volume of the sound is increased a whole band of the membrane is affected; the sound then tends towards noise (part of the continuous spectrum) and it becomes difficult to judge the pitch; practical experience of music verifies this. Since the basilar membrane is trapezoidal, the portions of the band on both sides of the objective frequency are not necessarily equal; a given sound seems to descend in pitch as its volume increases (up to about 2,000 Hz, when the phenomenon is reversed). Van Esbroeck thus explains the variation of pitch with intensity, but localization in the basilar membrane is far from proved.

brain (geniculate body)? Since Helmholtz, many authors have tended to locate it in the basilar membrane. This organ is something like a harp; if a low sound is produced, the low strings begin to vibrate by resonance; if a high note is produced, the high strings vibrate. The partisans of the basilar membrane theory then explain the augmentation of the sensation of intensity thus: they consider the basilar membrane to be trapezoidal in shape. A weak sinusoidal sound will excite one fibre only, and the same sound, produced with more intensity, will excite a *band* which will be larger according as the intensity is greater. But since the basilar membrane is trapezoidal, the widening of the band is not identical on both sides of the original frequency. For purely mechanical reasons, AB, for example, is smaller than AC for a frequency of excitation A. All the nerve cells between B and C then function, hence augmentation of the sensation of intensity. The wide band thus excited would be located by its middle (frequency perceived = frequency of arithmetical average between the limits B and C). From the fact of the trapezoidal shape of the membrane, an intense sound will seem *lower* than a weak one. This observation is confirmed below 2,000 Hz, but the phenomenon is inverted above this frequency. The phenomena are in reality very complex when musical sounds are in question (cf. Winckel, 144–50). Moreover, an intense sound will always contain sounds of neighbouring frequency; consequently an intense sound cannot be *pure*. But the theory of localization on the level of the basilar membrane is far from proved. I believe it too flagrantly contradicts certain physical laws. The internal ear is a strongly damped system; a damped system cannot be selective. But the ear is very sensitive in the selection of pitches. Under these conditions, the selection of pitches would seem to take place in the brain.

However that may be, in order to obtain intense sounds in music, it is preferable to enrich the spectrum by adding partials in the sensitive zone of the ear. In this way, one obtains great auditory intensity and a rich timbre at the same time. A great many lists of instrumental spectra have effectively shown that the best instruments offer a great spectral richness in the sensitive zone of the ear.

The subjective phenomena connected with audition have long been known. In a communication by Romieu to the Royal Society of Sciences at Montpellier, dated December 16, 1751, we read the following passage:

Wishing to tune a small organ pipe to the instrument called tone *or* diapason, *I placed both in my mouth in order to make them sound together and was surprised to hear, independently from their two distinct sounds, a third note, deep and very perceptible. I then raised the tone of the small pipe and a less deep note was the result. This note, when it is too low, seems thin and buzzes a little; but it becomes clearer and more mellow as it is raised. Long after my observation of this deep note eight or nine years ago, which I communicated to the Company on April 29, 1751, I discovered, by means of repeated experiments, that it was always the common inverted harmonic of the two sounds which produced it, so that for the number of its vibrations it had the highest common factor of the terms of their relation ...*

This means that two sounds emitted simultaneously and in given conditions produce a deeper sound of which the frequency is the highest common factor of the two component frequencies.

In 1915, in a report published in the *Comptes rendus de l'Académie des sciences* (vol. CLXI, 1915, pp. 634–781), Mr. Sizes pointed out:

By means of the Cavaillé-Coll experimental organ, invented by Mr. Mutin, which by combining the five last pipes (making an altogether discordant effect) makes the thirty-two first harmonics of C1 *vibrate, it is possible to produce the resonance of the common resulting sound* C1, *accompanied by the seventh harmonic* B♭3. *The same effect is obtained with the whole natural series.*

Thus it has been known since 1750 that two sounds could produce a deeper note, and more recently, that a group of neighbouring harmonics could restore the sensation of the fundamental. At that time there was no question of verifying whether this fundamental was objective or subjective, but organ builders knew how to make use of the method in order to obtain, with a series of small coupled pipes, some very deep notes, which would normally demand very large pipes (this is the 'acoustical bass' of English organ builders). The invention of electro-acoustical material has allowed us to prove that the deep frequency perceived does not exist objectively; it is the result of a reconstitution of the sensation of the fundamental, made by the brain from a group of harmonics close to the spectrum.

These problems have lately been revived (Schouten, 125; Winckel, 149; Meyer-Eppler, 92). For example, it is thanks to subjective audition that a very small loudspeaker can make us hear deep sounds, when it is by nature incapable of producing deep vibrations of sufficient amplitude. The subjective fundamental possesses a very special timbre, incisive and nasal, which can be identified with the French sound *in*, the objective fundamental being nearer the sound *oo* in 'moon'. Experiments have demonstrated that this subjective fundamental cannot be masked by an objective sound; therefore, it is certainly at the level of the brain that the phenomenon operates, and not on the basilar membrane.

Briefly, a musical sound, including many harmonics, can be characterized

by the predominance of the objective fundamental;

by the absence of the objective fundamental; in this case, it is the subjective fundamental which is heard, but the timbre is modified;

by a variable mixture of the two fundamentals.

What has been said explains certain points which have remained obscure, and which still remain the cause of many misunderstandings between musicians and physicists. Among others, there are:

1 The well-known fact that small-sized instruments (small violins, small violas or cellos) are always deficient on the deep notes and have a nasal timbre; it is the predominance of the subjective fundamental which is to blame.

2 The difficulty found by instrument makers in constructing violins with sufficiently rich bass (G) notes. In fact, the numerous violin spectra I have studied show that the percentage of energy contained in the fundamental of the notes of the G string is weak, or even almost nothing, contrary to what is noticed with the other strings. This also confirms earlier experiments: Seashore (129) already discovered in an open G of the violin a 0.1 per cent intensity for the fundamental.

3 The 'mystery' of Italian sonority. The timbre of ancient instruments, especially Italian ones, is somewhat nasal, which is often pleasing. This is due to the fact that an instrument, long submitted to strains arising from tension in the strings, becomes more and more rigid. The deep notes (i.e., the objective fundamentals) gradually lose their amplitude, giving place to the subjective fundamentals; hence the modification of the timbre with the ageing of the instrument.

The importance of psycho-physiological phenomena has now been sufficiently brought out. They permit an auditory interpretation of the structure of the musical signals emitted by instruments. We must now examine the mechanism by which the signal emitted by the violin is generated.

The bow

Charron (28) has studied the mechanism of the friction of the string by a wheel with a rosined felly, and has settled the fundamental laws of transversal vibration. A rosined surface drawn over a string produces a saw-tooth relaxation curve. We know that the coefficient of friction of two bodies in contact diminishes with their speed relative to each other. The diminution of the coefficient of friction is particularly rapid with rosin; that is why it has always been used for bowed instruments. If we place the bow on a string and begin to draw it, the adherent power of the rosin enables us to remove the string from its position of equilibrium to the point at which the force of recoil in the string exceeds it. The string then rebounds abruptly; the rapidity of return is great and the friction weak. The string passes back through its position of equilibrium and goes beyond it up to the point where the recoil speed is cancelled. Let us measure the time on the abscissa and the amplitude on the ordinate; the transversal movement of the string is a relaxation oscillation.

Charron also studied the influence of the rapidity of passage and the pressure of the circular bow he used. It is obvious that this study is incomplete; the functioning of the hair of a normal bow is different from that of the hurdy-gurdy wheel. In fact, the normal hair, slightly stretched, possesses a considerable degree of freedom in the bowing, and a given point of the string, instead of vibrating in a planar lune as is the case of the wheel, describes a fusiform volume with an ovoid section. We can verify that this section becomes flatter as the hair is stretched further. Moreover, the hair adheres more easily in the middle than at the ends. With the stroke of a bow, the vibratory form therefore varies continually from the middle to the ends of the bow; therefore, a normal violin note is a fluctuating phenomenon. Besides that, since the string has a certain thickness, a tangential force is developed on its surface, at the point of contact with the hair, which makes the string revolve and causes torsional vibrations. If we add the other phenomena (longitudinal vibrations, etc.), we conclude that the movement of a string under friction is much more complicated than the simplified saw-tooth diagram would suggest. Therefore it is necessary to study the mechanism of the functioning of bowed strings in another way.

The transverse vibratory movement and the torsional movement of a string over which a bow is drawn are saw-tooth oscillations of relaxation.

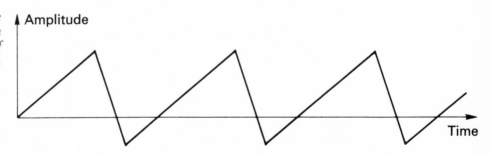

Functioning of the string

I have shown in other work (59–62) that, contrary to the simple hypotheses implicit in the elementary theory supplied by the treatises on physics, a string over which a bow is drawn vibrates in several ways, none of which is negligible, and that it is possible to isolate and study separately the following types of elementary movements shown in the illustration.

The well-known transverse vibration   Taylor has given the elementary formula of vibrating strings:

$$N_0 = \frac{1}{2L}\sqrt{\frac{T}{m}}.$$

This gives the fundamental frequency N_0 in relation to the length L, the total tension T of the string, and the linear bulk m. This formula only holds for theoretical strings (without tension); the real frequency N' of the partial of order q is in fact:

$$N' = qN_0\left(1 + \frac{E \cdot I}{T} \cdot \frac{q^2\pi^2}{2L^2}\right),$$

where E is Young's modulus for the material constituting the string and I is the moment of inertia of the right section in relation to an axis passing through the centre of inertia of the section and normal to the plane of vibration. This correction has important consequences: in practice, linear subdivisions of a string give elementary intervals only for strings of low tension. For example, if we divide a string into two equal parts, theoretically each half should give the octave of the entire string; in reality, we find that the octave is diminished according as the elastic modulus, the moment of inertia, and the number of the partial decrease, and the tension and the length increase.

Experience proves effectively that gut is preferable to steel, for example; that one should seek to get as close as possible to the maximum tension compatible with the string's resistance, and that it is advisable to use very long strings.

The influence of string tension upon playing technique also varies according to whether or not the instruments have frets. For instruments with a smooth fingerboard (i.e., when the vibrating length is determined by the finger), tension has no theoretical importance in ensuring the accuracy of intervals, since the player, by acquired competence, instinctively corrects by ear the position of his finger on the fingerboard. But in practice, the problem is complicated by the fact that the neighbouring strings of a violin have neither the same diameter nor the same elastic modulus nor the same tension. In consequence, for each of the instrument's strings the correction is different, and the position of the fingers on the fingerboard is not the same for all four strings. The phenomenon is particularly clear on the violoncello, and constitutes a considerable annoyance for players with a keen ear. I have known talented players who solved the problem thus: since strings made of gut are all more or less conical, they feel with their fingers the direction in which the strings should run in order to arrive at an acceptable compromise. In fact, one can find strings the conicity of which compensates for the effects of tension, and then the instrumentalist plays absolutely in tune, because the fifths and the octaves are *at the same level* on the fingerboard.

The tension of the strings, therefore, has a notable influence on the accuracy of the player's notes, and it is more difficult than is generally believed to string an unfretted instrument correctly. The problem of accuracy in strings thus takes on a paradoxical aspect. The physicist calls *true* a string in which frequency is inversely proportional to length; taking stiffness into account he is led to admit that a real string is true when various equal segments of it give the same frequency. Now these definitions are not enough for the musician; he calls *true* those strings which have their fifths, octaves, etc. at the same level on the fingerboard. Given the difference in tension between the neighbouring strings on the same instrument, one is led to use strings of different conicity, which are, therefore, physically inaccurate. Hence we get the paradoxical conclusion: one can only play accurately with inaccurate strings; a string is only accurate in relation to the neighbouring strings.

The problem is more complex still with fretted instruments like the guitar. The frets settle the vibrating lengths once and for all, but the distances between the frets only hold for strings of well-determined tension. Since commercial manufacture is far from invariable, in order to limit inaccuracy the frets are usually stopped at two-thirds of the total length of the string. In the time when guitar players used strings made of gut, it was possible for them to take advantage of the conicity of the strings, but now strings are made of nylon or metal (with great regularity of calibration) and the octaves cannot be at the same level on the fingerboard. An attempt has been made to remedy this by sloping the frets as the player runs up the fingerboard; this corrects the tension to a certain extent, but the method only holds good for a well-defined type of string. In desperation, a small individual bridge for each string has been employed for guitars with steel strings, so that each one can be corrected according to its own tension. The correction for tension is thus a very troublesome procedure in the stringing of instruments, because it affects accuracy in playing.

But that is not all; the tension of the strings also affects the timbre. Indeed, since the real frequency of a segment differs from the theoretical frequency in inverse proportion to the square of the vibrating length, the result is that the harmonics of a string become progressively more inaccurate (they are thus no longer harmonics but partials) as their pitch goes higher. This is the case for muted strings (plucked, struck) and the more they are corrected for tension, the less pleasing their timbre becomes. The problem is different for strings in sustained motion. Experiments prove that the sustained note is indeed a periodical phenomenon, the partials of which come back into the harmonic series. This is only possible if the partials can be accommodated to the harmonics according to a process inherent in the sustaining mechanism of sound. However, the accommodation is effected with a loss of energy proportional to the distance between the partials and the corresponding harmonics. In other words, for a string in sustained motion, the harmonic spectrum will be poorer and the strength deficient according as the correction of tension is greater; and this is borne out by experience. It is in our interest therefore to diminish this correction as much as possible by regulating the physical parameters to best advantage. The most efficient way is to augment the length, because the square of length is part of the formula.

The longitudinal vibration In vibrating transversely, the musical strings are periodically prolonged, because of their elasticity; thus, longitudinal vibration is excited. This vibration can be isolated and brought into evidence very simply by drawing the bow down the string lengthways so that it makes a very small angle with the string. Then one usually hears a very high note several octaves above the transverse fundamental.

As a first approximation, the longitudinal fundamental frequency can be given by the formula

$$N_l = \frac{1}{2L} \sqrt{\frac{E}{\rho}},$$

E being always the elastic modulus and ρ indicating the volumetric mass of the material. Experiments made with the help of many subjects have proved that this longitudinal vibration determines the more or less high character of the string's timbre. For example, it differentiates the steel string from the gut string. This longitudinal frequency can be heard especially well when it coincides with a harmonic of transverse vibration, because then a resonance phenomenon is produced. One can regulate the parameters relative to longitudinal frequency so as to obtain a resonance on any transverse harmonic, according to the musical effect desired. The formula indicated, however, only holds good insofar as the mechanical characteristics, and consequently the longitudinal vibration, are independent of the tension of the string. Now, if that is largely correct for some materials (steel, gut), it is not so for others (nylon, for example) the structure of which is modified by pressures.

Torsional vibration Simple experiments – observation under the microscope of one point of the string, movements of a thin strip of paper stuck straight onto the string, etc. – prove that when a bow is drawn across the string it vibrates torsionally under the influence of the tangential force developed by the hair. These are torsional relaxation oscillations, as can be demonstrated. They can easily be heard; it suffices to press hard enough on the string with the bow so as to mute the transversal oscillations. We then see the string become immobile (there is no longer a lune of noteworthy amplitude) and we hear a deep note the frequency of which is several tones lower than the transverse frequency and which, for a given transverse sound, depends largely on the physical nature of the strings. These notes play the part of a deep component of the timbre, a phenomenon identical with the well-known one observed in the sounds of bells.

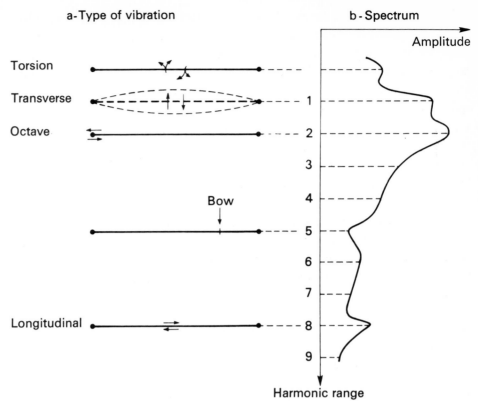

The frequency of torsion is set down thus

$$N_r = \frac{1}{2L}\sqrt{\frac{G}{\rho}},$$

where G is the tension modulus and ρ is the volumetric mass. Vibration from torsion partially explains the variations of the acoustical qualities of strings connected with these two parameters.

The vibration of the octave Let us fasten one end of a string to the centre of a membrane and then strike it transversely. It has long been known (Raman, 113) that the membrane gives a sound an octave higher than the string. In fact, let us consider the vibrating lune: for each half-lune, between the rest position and the end positions, the string exercises a traction on its fastened points which then vibrate with a frequency double that of the string. If the fixed point is an organ of sufficient surface and possesses a degree of appropriate freedom, the *octave vibration* can become an important element in the spectrum.

This is precisely the case for stringed instruments when the fixed points communicate with the tables. The octave vibration is connected with the same physical parameters as the transverse vibration; it systematically modifies the harmonic 2 in the spectrum of the string. Numerous analyses have shown us that in fact the harmonic 2 has a considerable volume, very often superior to that of the fundamental.

To sum up, the signal emitted by a string is determined by the four preceding vibratory modes, their combination, and their reactions. We can formulate the shape of the excitation thus: let us represent the transverse frequency and its respective harmonics by a curve with points (A, n), in which A is the amplitude and n the frequency, and then draw the enveloping curve of this transverse spectrum. We know that it is the shape of the enveloping curve of a spectrum which determines the auditory appreciation of the sound, as the works of physiologists like Licklider (77) have demonstrated. If this shape is simple, without accidental variations, the sound lacks character. But if the longitudinal frequency coincides with one of the harmonics of the transverse frequency (the eighth, for example) it produces on the reference curve a *swell* of resonance which we call a *positive formant* because it contributes to *forming* the timbre, to giving it its character and quality. We may also measure on the graph the positive formants arising from the torsional frequency and the octave vibration in order to obtain the characteristic shape of the excitation of the box by the mobile system of bowstrings.

Other factors which intervene in the functioning of the string
In reality, things are not so beautifully simple. A great many exterior factors intervene to modify the shape of the excitation.

Place of the bow on the string   The bow divides the vibrating length into two unequal parts. The textbooks tell us that since the point of contact between bow and string is an antinode, all the harmonics having a node placed on this point cannot be produced. For example, if the bow touches the string at one-fifth of its length, the harmonic 5 cannot appear, and in the spectrum a hole is produced on this harmonic, *a negative formant*, which modifies the spectrum of excitation, that is, the quality of the sound. It is a phenomenon empirically well known to violinists: the variations of timbre related to the position of the bow form part of the effects of violin playing, and are indeed an important part of it. But this is just a schematic explanation. In actual fact, the bow does not touch one point on the string, but a whole segment (about 1 cm); thus the hair covers a whole series of harmonic nodes (for example, harmonics 6–12–18; 13; 7–14; 15; 8–16). But the phenomena are more complex still; to be convinced of this, one has only to record a series of spectra produced as the point of contact is changed. The law is further complicated by the problems of the link between string and instrument. One thing is certain, the spectrum of a note is profoundly transformed when we change the point of contact. In consequence, the sound spectrum from the violin has meaning only to the extent that the point of contact is specified.

Role of humidity   Musical strings are traditionally made of sheep-gut, steel, or nylon. The best adapted material for the traditional violin is gut for the A–D–G strings, often wound with a thread of metal which makes it possible to increase the average density of the string, and therefore to diminish the diameters and consequently the tension. Now, gut is essentially hygroscopic, which means

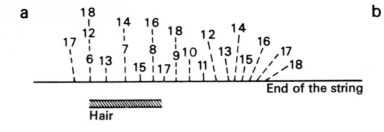

a

18
12
14
16
18
12
14
17
6 13
7
8
9 10
13
16
17
15
17
11
15
18

Hair

End of the string

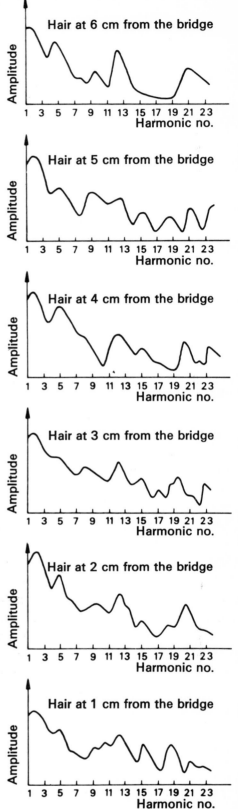

b

Hair at 6 cm from the bridge

Amplitude

1 3 5 7 9 11 13 15 17 19 21 23
Harmonic no.

Hair at 5 cm from the bridge

Amplitude

1 3 5 7 9 11 13 15 17 19 21 23
Harmonic no.

Hair at 4 cm from the bridge

Amplitude

1 3 5 7 9 11 13 15 17 19 21 23
Harmonic no.

Hair at 3 cm from the bridge

Amplitude

1 3 5 7 9 11 13 15 17 19 21 23
Harmonic no.

Hair at 2 cm from the bridge

Amplitude

1 3 5 7 9 11 13 15 17 19 21 23
Harmonic no.

Hair at 1 cm from the bridge

Amplitude

1 3 5 7 9 11 13 15 17 19 21 23
Harmonic no.

Fluctuations of spectra affected by the point of contact. a. The perceptible harmonics vary with the position of the hair on the string. The hair of the violin bow is about 1 cm wide. Therefore it always covers a certain number of the string's vibratory nodes, the correlative harmonics of which are the perceptible harmonics of the bow. It will be noted that the place of the bow conditions the numbers of the perceptible harmonics. On the other hand, the violinist can systematically modify the number of perceptible harmonics by inclining the hair to a greater or lesser degree. According to the aesthetic effect desired, he employs a width of hair varying from a millimetre to a centimetre. b. Evolution of the spectrum with the point of contact: on the abscissa the figures of the harmonics, on the ordinate the amplitudes. The spectrum changes considerably; the subjective effect is well known to instrumentalists. Here the violin's open G was produced by gradually drawing the bow across the string between 1 and 6 cm from the bridge, and the spectrum was recorded at every centimetre. We see that the real phenomena are much more complex than the elementary theory would indicate. Generally speaking, at 6 cm from the bridge (sul tasta) the spectrum shows holes; near the bridge it is much richer, especially in high harmonics (from 15 to 19). The auditory effect is well known to violinists. In a very large measure the bow allows a systematic modelling of the spectrum. It is known that the technique of the right hand is a capital element in the violinist's 'sonority.'

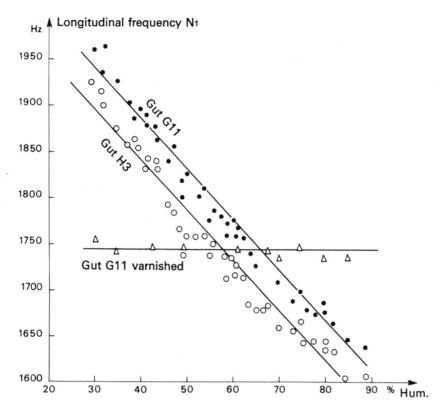

Effect of humidity on a gut string. We can see that the longitudinal frequency of the string varies widely with humidity; correlatively the timbre, i.e. the spectrum of the string, changes. This frequency drops about a major third, an enormous variation. The consequences are well known to violinists; when the weather is damp the timbre changes and the instrument's sound is less clear. The modification of the muting co-efficient then complicates the problem still further.

there are large and important variations in its elastic properties, and consequently in the longitudinal frequency. In the samples given in the illustration, for example, we see that for an increase in humidity from 20 to 90 per cent, the longitudinal frequency drops from 1,950 to 1,600 Hz. which corresponds to about a major third. It is quite obvious that under these conditions the timbre alters with humidity, as all violinists know. To avoid this inconvenience, one can varnish the string, and the longitudinal frequency then no longer varies. Experience proves, however, that this protection is rather illusory, because the strings are constantly rubbed by the nails and fingers. This explains the popularity of steel strings with professional violinists; but these strings, while insensible to humidity, have other drawbacks: they have practically no capacity for extension, hence the pitch of a note is modified when more pressure is put on the bow; their timbre is more shrill on account of the very high longitudinal frequency; their muting coefficient is too weak, etc.

Thus, the sound spectrum of a string is modified according to the degree of humidity. This phenomenon was empirically known; the modification of the longitudinal frequency explains it. Humidity also affects the muting coefficient of gut strings, as is shown by a general lowering of the amplitudes of the different harmonics (which is why the timbre becomes duller) and by a lengthening of the attack transient as humidity increases (i.e. the attack of the note becomes less percussive).

The stabilization of the strings   It is known that a musical string of gut or nylon subjected to fairly high tensions lengthens after the initial tuning; the reason is

Stabilization of the strings. The traditional gut or nylon strings do not 'sound' normally when the instrument has just been strung; they stretch gradually and the timbre alters. Violinists say that the string 'adjusts itself'; it reaches an optimum, then deteriorates and 'dies.' Good players do not wait for it to break or become worn before replacing it. These facts, familiar to players, are clearly demonstrated in the figure above: it shows how six gut strings evolve if subjected to fixed tension for six months. Their longitudinal frequency rises continually. If the auditive optimum is at 1,730 Hz, for example, the strings reach this point more or less quickly, taking between one hour and three months. Briefly then, strings stabilize more or less rapidly according to the quality of the materials used. There is a certain margin of tolerance round the optimum value, but above this margin the string is 'dead,' it is acoustically worn out.

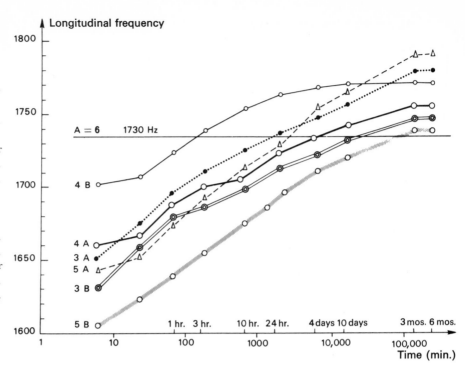

that elastic materials become deformed in time if they are subjected to sufficient pressures. Correlatively, the timbre alters for a time that varies according to circumstances; the instrumentalist says that the string *adjusts itself.* In order to study this phenomenon, I have measured the longitudinal frequency of a good many strings and observed important variations. The illustration shows six gut strings, the longitudinal frequency of which was measured at the start (eight minutes after stringing); for each of these strings we observe a constant rise of the longitudinal frequency as time progresses. Thus from eight minutes to six months string 5B passes from 1,600 to 1,730 Hz. Therefore, all during this time the spectrum of the string evolves gradually. The general progress of the curves of these six strings is about the same. One notes, however, that the string 4B rises to about 1,760 and after ten days of tension hardly moves again; it has stabilized. This stabilization, which is relative, occurs at a more or less high frequency; it is reached more or less rapidly according to the materials used. Consequently, if 1,730 Hz, for example, is the maximum longitudinal frequency for a given string, it is clear that this state is reached more or less rapidly according to the kind of string (three hours for the string 4D; six months for the string 5B).

On the other hand, after reaching the optimum, the curves continue to rise. When the optimum is passed the string deteriorates, it *dies.* This explains why good musicians change their strings before they break or are worn out.

We may add that some materials which, like nylon, are very liable to become deformed, have stabilization curves completely different from those of gut; steel, for example, hardly alters at all. Stabilization also entails a modification of the muting coefficient.

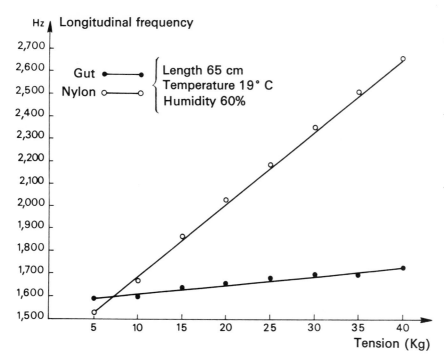

Role of tension. When a string is stretched gradually, not only does its frequency rise, but also there is an alteration in the nature of its timbre. By way of example, a nylon and a gut string are compared here. The longitudinal frequency has been measured between 5 and 40 kg. If this frequency changes, the timbre alters. We observe that gut is very stable from this point of view: its longitudinal frequency varies little with tension (between 1,600 and 1,700 Hz). It is not the same with nylon. The longitudinal frequencies of the two types of strings cross at about 7 kg (intersection of the two straight lines); the more the tension increases, the more they diverge and the more different the timbres become. We understand why it is not possible to obtain the same result in sonority from different materials. We see also the interest in the traditional material, gut.

Influence of tension   In the preceding case we have considered the modifications in the longitudinal frequency of a string subjected to a fixed tension for a variable period. But if one stretches a string gradually, one also observes a modification of the longitudinal frequency with the tension and independent of time. For example, suppose we stretch a string with a force of 5 kg and measure the longitudinal frequency; then we immediately augment the tension by 5 kg increments and plot the curve of the frequency variations. Consider two typical examples. Gut hardly rises between 5 and 40 kg (from 1,600 to 1,700 Hz); nylon, on the contrary, rises considerably (from 1,500 to 2,600 Hz). The two straight lines cross at about 7 kg. At this tension, the two strings have the same longitudinal frequency, but they diverge very widely after that. This explains (apart from other points, e.g. muting) why it is impossible to use nylon if we wish to obtain an identical result in sonority to that of gut. Similarity of timbre only exists for one tension.

All this amply proves that the mere theoretical formulae of longitudinal vibrations, in themselves quite inadequate, can only show us the meaning, the general behaviour of the phenomena. If the experimental method allows us to obtain accurate results fairly easily with the help of measurements, we should have few illusions about the results our calculations will achieve; the problems of real strings are simple only in appearance. It remains true nonetheless that the parameters which influence the quality of a string can largely be regulated systematically, and it is they that determine the shape of the excitation. This shape being defined, we still have to show how its amplification and distortion are produced by the instrument, in order to derive finally the spectrum radiated by the instrument.

Let us look at the longitudinal section of the violin. At the outset a certain amount of energy is involved in the force of contact between bow and string; this energy is shared between the various vibratory modes, which communicate it to the instrument proper:

> the transverse and torsional vibrations are communicated to the table by means of the bridge DE, then to the back by the sound post FG;
> the longitudinal and octave vibrations are transmitted to the front by the points of attachment B and C (buckling vibrations) and to the back by the points H and I.

The quantitative sharing of the energy depends on the structure of the system, especially on the angle of the strings on the bridge (angle ADC). If this angle is very small, the transversal and torsional vibrations will play the chief role; if it is very large, the longitudinal and octave vibrations will dominate. In the first case, the general timbre will be deeper, more sombre, as in the violoncello; in the second it will be clearer, as in the guitar. These shades, however, are obtained on one violin by altering the height of the bridge; the auditory result is empirically familiar to instrument makers.

The diagram on the right shows the mechanism of the violin. The reality is more complex, and it will be well to supply a few more precise points of information. Let us examine the cross section of the violin at the bridge-point and the elevation of the table at the same point. We see that the right foot (d) of the bridge rests on the table at a small distance from the point of contact between the sound post and the table (ad = about 5 mm). The left foot (g) rests on the bass bar: gd = 30 mm. This remarkable arrangement achieves two very different degrees of freedom at the right and left feet of the bridge; a simple pressure of the thumbs on the top allows us to verify that the left foot can be pressed down much more easily than the right foot. The efficacity of the arrangement is further increased by the fact that pine wood is much more

Diagram of the violin's mechanism. The force communicated to the string by the bow is applied to the bridge and to the points of attachment of the strings A and C. The distribution of the energy depends on the angle of the strings over the bridge, ADC. Instrument makers know empirically that the regulation of this angle affects the sound of the violin.

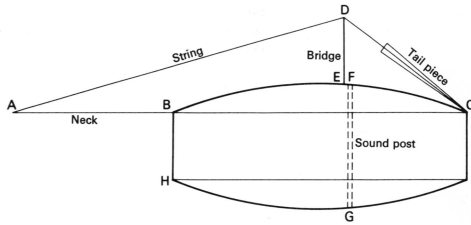

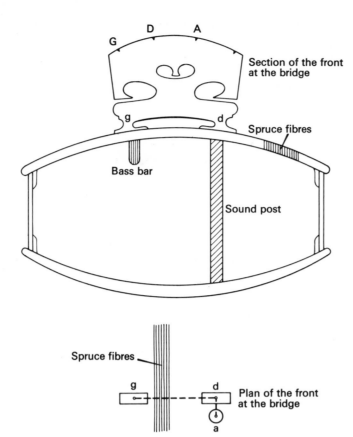

Section of the front
at the bridge

Spruce fibres

Bass bar

Sound post

Spruce fibres

Plan of the front
at the bridge

*Section of the violin at the height of the bridge.
Three points are acoustically important: the
two feet of the bridge and the top of the sound post
placed a few millimetres behind the right foot.
The degree of freedom of these three points can
in large measure be regulated (a) by the
thicknesses of the tables and the dimensions of the
bass bar as well as its positioning, (b) by the
distances between right foot and left foot and
between right and foot sound post. The final
regulation of the violin consists in modifying the
distance ad so as to obtain optimum sound
production.*

flexible in the tranverse direction of the fibres than in the direction of the grain.
The high strings depend on the right foot, which is relatively fixed with a slight
degree of freedom, and the low strings depend on the left foot, which has a
considerable degree of freedom. It is thanks to this arrangement that the violin
amplifies almost homogeneously over a range of more than four and a half
octaves.

One can easily demonstrate the differences in the properties of the two points
of the table corresponding to the two feet of the bridge. If a small hollow glass
tube (2 to 3 mm in diameter) is placed at one of the points, and rubbed lengthwise with a finger moistened with acidic water, we hear a note the frequency of
which depends on the degree of freedom of the point under study. For example,
with one violin my results were as follows: right foot, 790 Hz (about G4);
left foot, 476 Hz (about Bb3), that is, about the interval of a sixth. It is obvious
that this interval varies considerably from one instrument to another, according
to the elastic parameters of the wood employed, the thicknesses of the tables,
the dimensions and rigidity of the bass bar, the relation ad/dg, and the characteristics of the back (connected through the sound post at the point d). With
the instrument entirely finished, the maker can still regulate the degrees of
freedom of the feet of the bridge by regulating the sound post, that is, by varying the distance between the sound post and the right foot.

The response curve   The strings are then joined to the body of the instrument. The connection coefficients depend, on the one hand, on the material, dimensions, and shape of the bridge (the larger the portions cut out, the slacker will be the connection), and on the other hand, on the mobility of the attachment points of the strings (this varies with the size of the neck, the thickness of the corner blocks, etc.). The empirical regulation by the craftsman of these connection coefficients constitutes an important part of the instrument maker's general art, because it is on all these connecting points and on the damping characteristics of the materials that the evenness of the instrument, that is, the regularity of the different notes produced by it, largely depends.

In every case, the excitation signal is communicated to the instrument, which can be considered as a compact group of resonators each with its own individual frequency. The distinctness of these resonators can be easily shown. By the mere friction of the bow one can excite the frequency of the tail piece, of the fingerboard, of the bridge, of the head, etc. One can also use electromagnetic or electrostatic methods.

ABOVE   *the response curve of a violin, determined by the fundamental frequencies peculiar to each constituent part of the instrument. We see that a great many of the elementary frequencies are grouped in the sensitive zone of the ear (about 300–3,000 Hz).* BELOW   *response curve of an Amati violin taken by acoustical spectrograph. The spectrum radiated is the result of the combination of the excitation curve with the response curve. To have a homogeneous instrument, there must be an even response curve; if the materials have a strong coefficient of inner friction, the peaks are levelled; hence the justification for the use of the traditional materials: gut, wood, soft varnishes, etc.*

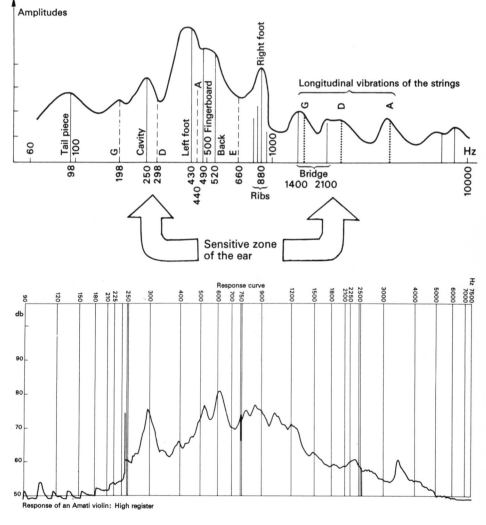

On a graph, let us plot the frequencies of these various resonators along the abscissa, and their amplitudes along the ordinate. If we draw the enveloping curve of these different resonators, while taking into account their respective muting properties, we obtain the *response curve* of the instrument.

Several authors have endeavoured to make lists of such curves; they vary infinitely with violins on account of the diversity of materials used and the differences in structure from one instrument maker to another. In fine, it is the instrument maker who is responsible for the shape of the response curve. Reproduced here by way of example is a response curve taken by direct excitation of the various parts of a violin. I prefer this direct method to the electromagnetic or electrostatic method, because these last introduce the respective partials of the fundamental frequencies of each resonator, and in so doing complicate the response curves so much that it becomes impossible to use or to analyse them. I have also listed many response curves produced by striking the instrument at given points. In the very complex curves thus obtained, one can discern the influence of the frequencies proper to the various parts of the instrument, and show that the instrument maker can act at will upon the spectral curve.

It is quite obvious that a homogeneous response curve is desirable in instrument making; otherwise some notes would be shrill and others weak. Holes in the curve and overly strong resonances must therefore be avoided; this is, on the whole, the principal difficulty in making the sound box of the instrument. Craftsmen can overcome this difficulty more or less successfully in the light of experience (with all the elements of chance which this includes), but it can quite as well be overcome by scientific control at the time the instrument is being constructed.

To sum up, the signal radiated by the violin results from the combination of the shape of the excitation curve with the instrument's response curve as just defined. When a positive formant of the excitation curve coincides with a point of resonance in the response curve, we get a super-resonance in the signal radiated; when coincidence occurs between a negative formant of the excitation curve and a hole in the response curve, we get a rejection, an anti-resonance, in the signal radiated by the instrument.

The all-important consequence is that the response curve is fixed on the scale of frequencies and determined once and for all by the instrument maker, but the shape of the excitation curve varies and changes continually on the scale of frequencies during normal playing of the instrument. Since the response curve is never linear and shows a great number of irregularities, it is evident that *the signal radiated by the instrument alters in shape with each note emitted*. I have verified this by a great many listings of the spectra of violins and other instruments.

In these conditions:

1 It is impossible to speak of the *spectrum of such and such an instrument*, since the spectrum changes in shape with each note; consequently it is impossible to define the timbre of an instrument solely by its spectrum as a permanent law.

2 Since the permanent spectrum is not significant, how can the ear distinguish the timbre of the violin from that of the clarinet or the oboe? In other words,

which are the invariable elements in the *sound* of the violin, the clarinet, etc.? The answer is obtainable in experiments easy to carry out with a tape recorder; notes from musical instruments are recorded and then the part of the sounds corresponding to the attacks and the extinctions are cut off with scissors. The sounds being thus amputated, it often becomes impossible to identify the instrument which produced them. Therefore *it is the transient factors* (shape, gradation, order of the appearance of partials, extinction) *which allow us to recognize the nature of the instrument*; the spectrum as a permanent law only determines the differences of quality within a given type of instrument.

Since transients are connected with the mode of attack and the muting of the vibrating system, the sound of the violin is therefore essentially recognized by the type of excitation in the bow and strings. One can be easily convinced of this by fixing violin strings on any kind of box and recording a melody of unvarying volume. A listener unaware of the experiment will say without hesitation, 'That is violin music.' Savart's experiment (123) with his trapezoidal violin (a body quite different from that of the classic violin) is significant in this respect; without looking, no one could distinguish precisely the trapezoidal violin from the ordinary one, and yet musicians like Cherubini were members of the commission that judged Savart's violin.

Briefly then, the spectrum as a permanent law is not significant of the type of instrument but it is a criterion of its quality.

Sonogram of a violin by Gabrielly, 1767. The sonograph allows the recording of the evolution of the spectrum over time. The sonogram consists of three parts: (a) the volume recording of each note. (b) The recording of the spectral evolution: the four open strings have been played; each note lasts about half a second. The harmonics are shown by lines that become blacker as the volume of the harmonic increases; they are to be read from the bottom upwards. For example, the harmonics 5 and 10 of the note G are important. (c) A section – spectrum – is made at the interesting points in the recording. Here the harmonics are read from top to bottom; their amplitudes are measured on a logarithmic scale; this is the classic spectrum.

Many recordings with the sonograph have shown that: (a) There are as many shapes of spectra as there are notes; so one cannot speak of the 'spectrum of a violin.' (b) The spectrum of one note varies continuously with the instrumental technique, the left hand (bowing) technique, and the right hand technique in shortening the strings. The normal playing of the instrument is a continuous kaleidoscopic shimmering of timbres; the unvarying factor of the violin's sound lies in the transients, which achieve unity in variety.

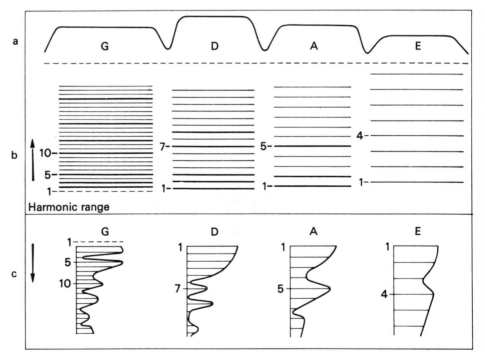

The problem of the appreciation of sonority was insoluble before the invention of electro-acoustical apparatus and techniques. The dispute over ancient and modern violins is a typical example. It is generally admitted that the Stradivari models are the best violins in the world, but early experiments known as 'sonority contests' were far from conclusive on this point.

Sonority contests were organized at the beginning of this century. There was no question then of carrying out systematic research work in a laboratory. In those days there was no possibility of adequate recording or analysis. An audience, more or less selected, assembled in a certain hall. A number of instruments were played without being seen, and the listeners were asked to classify them in order. Therefore it was a matter of subjective judgments. The first of these contests was held in Paris in 1909, and the organizer stated its aim.

Our role consists in organizing a completely unprejudiced experiment which will permit connoisseurs to pass a purely auditive judgement, uninfluenced by the fact that they are hearing an instrument valued at one hundred thousand francs.

Therefore the problem was to find out whether it was possible to distinguish by ear between an ancient and a modern violin. The answer was negative; a modern violin by Gand and Bernardel placed first, ahead of a Stradivari and other ancient instruments. The Gaveau hall, used for the tests, was empty for the eliminating trials, and full for the final one.

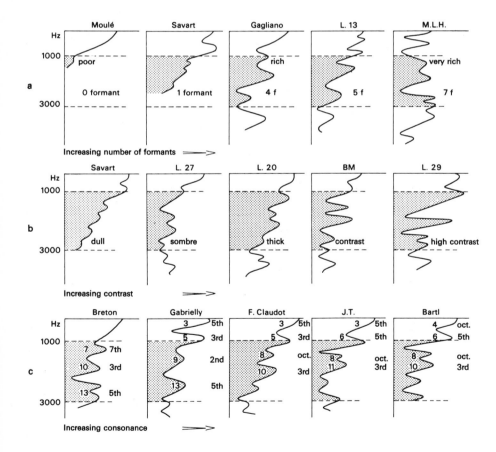

Analysis of spectrograms (sonograms). Three sets of instruments have been classified in order of: (a) 'richness' of timbre (increasing number of formants); (b) 'contrast' of sound (increasing contrast of formants); (c) consonance-dissonance (harmonic relation between harmonics and fundamental). The sensitive zone of the ear (1,000 to 3,000 Hz) has been shaded: what takes place there is auditively important.

In 1910 a contest for violoncellos was held in the Salle des Agriculteurs, under similar conditions. In the final test a new instrument obtained the preference and won 465 points against 288 accorded to a Stradivari. Nevertheless, the instrument classed first in the final audition had been last in the eliminating one.

In 1912 another contest for violins was held again in the Salle des Agriculteurs. In the final test the two first instruments were modern. The instrument at the head of the list in the first eliminating test was placed last in the second, only to end up first in the final. By contrast, the instrument classed last at the first eliminating test headed the list in the second, only to be last again in the final test. Chenantais (29) explains these anomalies by the modifications of the characteristics of the hall, full or empty according to the occasion.

Another violin contest was held in 1921 in the hall of the Paris Conservatory. Two modern violins led the list, ahead of a Stradivari. The violinist was asked to give his impressions. His personal classification was almost the exact opposite of that of the listeners.

1 It is clear, then, that if no hint has been given beforehand it is impossible to distinguish an old instrument from a new one by ear alone. The superior sonority of a Stradivari and others is a myth; there are good and bad instruments in every period – that is all.

2 Opinions seem to fluctuate haphazardly when we compare the eliminating trials and the final classifications. It is certain that an instrument does not sound the same in an empty hall as in a full one. We know why this is, now that considerable progress has been made in the acoustics of halls since 1921. One can compare instruments only in identical hearing conditions; there is no absolute judgment of value, since a soloist's instrument is intended for playing in a large hall, and an instrument for a member of a quartet is made for a small enclosed locality.

3 The judgment of the player is different from that of the listener, because he hears the instrument from a distance of inches; his opinion only holds good for himself, in his particular position.

4 Sonority depends largely on the player; we have seen how he influences the spectrum of excitation. The reputation of Stradivari violins is due in great part to the fact that only the gifted virtuosi could buy them, on account of the exorbitant prices demanded for them (up to one hundred thousand francs before the war of 1914). In the hands of an unskilful violinist even a Stradivari becomes common!

5 Ear fatigue during the tests plays a considerable part in the listener's judgment. Other elements intervene also, including temperature and hygrometry.

Notwithstanding these contests the essential difficulty remains of assessing accurately the acoustical quality of a violin, since there are many parameters liable to warp the judgment. The contests have been valuable nonetheless in revealing the failure of subjective judgment and in proving the necessity of studying a musical instrument's quality from objective bases. The existence of electro-acoustical material and techniques allows this problem to be taken up again under satisfactory conditions. In fact, we are now able to determine without difficulty the whole range of sonorous phenomena, thanks to recording techniques; the appearance of the tape recorder was decisive here. We can therefore work upon documents, reproduce the phenomenon at will, preserve it, analyse it in the laboratory with the aid of the material we now have – volume-recording instruments, spectrographs, oscillographs, etc. It is no longer a problem of apparatus but of method. How should we carry out recordings and measurements? Which parameters should be recorded and measured? How should the results be interpreted?

RECORDINGS AND MEASUREMENTS

Sonority contests have shown that the instrumentalist should be eliminated. One should use, for example, a mechanical bow, the parameters of which (rapidity of passage, tension, 'pressure' on the strings) can be regulated; besides that, instead of a melody, one should only play notes or scales.

The influence of the hall should also be eliminated by recording in a sound-proof hall, or at least one with very little reverberation. We must have a well-adapted technique for recording the sounds. The notes should be recorded on a first-class tape recorder with the aid of appropriate microphones and then analysed and studied in the laboratory. It is now possible to visualize acoustical phenomena; this puts an objective foundation of documents at our disposal. The technical problem is solved.

Every acoustical phenomenon can be defined by means of three dimensions: volume, frequency, and time.

Volume The sensation of *power* of a sound is connected with acoustical pressure. On account of the properties of the ear, a logarithmic scale is used. The decibel concept is now widespread. We know that in the sensitive zone of the

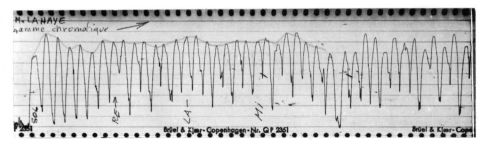

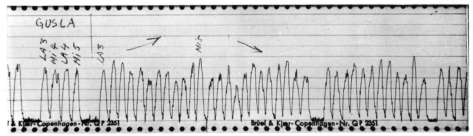

A volume recording permits the direct reading of the average volume of the instrument and its 'homogeneity,' its 'evenness' (volume differences between the various notes). The top chart is a volume analysis of a remarkably homogeneous instrument; below it, the volume analysis of a gusla, a small primitive monochord.

ear a volume difference of 3 db is clearly perceptible. Modern recording devices (logarithmic bathymeters) solve the problems of volume recording without difficulty. It is easy to play a scale on a violin and record the volume of the notes produced. Such a recording gives a calculated value for the average volume of the instrument, and also for the homogeneity, that is, the divergences of volume between the different notes.

The various parameters which determine the auditive quality of the instrument are measured on the table of the violin's charactersitics. They are given a settled coefficient, and a total is obtained which permits an objective opinion to be formed on the general acoustical value of the violin in question. It becomes possible to classify a series of instruments after the fashion of sonority contests. The table gives a real acoustical photograph of the violin. It should be accompanied by the following documents: (a) a photograph of the instrument; (b) the recording tapes preserving the 'sonorous objects'; (c) the instrument's response curve; (d) the characteristics of the strings; (e) the excitation characteristics: type of bow, rapidity of passage, pressure on the strings, point of contact, etc. It goes without saying that the conditions for the recording must be strictly standardized and that the material used must be accurately described. The coefficients may be modified according to circumstances; thus, when an instrument is intended for recorded music, the volume coefficient can take second place, to the benefit of the spectrum.

TABLE OF CHARACTERISTICS

Apparatus used	Parameters	Coefficient	Number of points out of 5	Total
Decibelmeter or volume recorder	Average volume	4	4	16
	'Evenness' (homogeneity)	3	3	9
Spectrograph	Richness of the spectrum	4	4	16
Analyser	Consonance of the formants	3	4	12
Sonograph	Contrast of the formants	3	2	6
Oscillograph + motion picture camera	Gradation of attack transient (in db/second)	2	3	6
	Gradation of extinction transient	1	3	3
Total out of 100				68

Frequencies The problems of frequencies are of two types: those of the musical accuracy of instruments and those of timbre.

1 The problem of accuracy is easy to study now that we have frequency meters of all kinds (such as acoustical stroboscopes and low-frequency generators allowing us to obtain Lissajous figures); these devices permit precise measurements of pitch, and it is possible to form an opinion on the accuracy of the playing or of the internal harmony of instruments from any scale of reference (e.g. the musical scale).

2 The problem of timbre is much more delicate. But modern spectrographs (various analysers, the sonograph, etc.) enable us to materialize the spectrum of any musical sound without difficulty.

Time The evolution of an acoustical phenomenon in time is easy to photograph by means of the oscillograph and cinematic camera; thus without complications we can measure the duration of transient factors, and appreciate their shape, their gradation, etc. Briefly, then, the visual three-dimensional representation of a sound is now possible and the significant parameters are well known; the real difficulty lies in interpreting the documents.

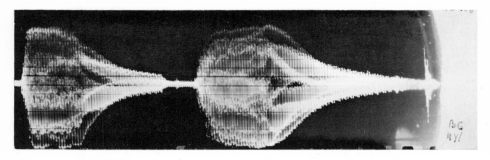

INTERPRETATION

In essence, this is a question of knowing the correlation between the documents recorded and the auditive perception. We have already seen what difficulties we are up against in studying the psycho-physiology of audition. The results obtained are in need of continuous interpretation because the apparatus does not function like the ear-brain system, and they can only be interpreted by a specialist. Thus an abstract of the statement of volume must be made in relation to the isotonic curves of the ear; from the notion of decibels we pass to phones, still insufficient because the volume of a sound is connected with the timbre, with the shape of the spectrum. In fact, we have seen that the brain is capable of restoring the sensation of the fundamental from a group of harmonics; the *subjective fundamental*, by definition, has no physical existence. Nevertheless it is apparent to our senses, though its volume, being likewise subjective and therefore a purely psychic phenomenon, obviously cannot be measured by any volume recording instrument. This observation explains certain divergences of opinion between physicists and musicians about the volume of sounds, as well as discussions among musicians about the distinction between the *volume* of a sound and its *range*.

The interpretation of the qualities of timbre from the spectra is no easier, but their enveloping curve allows us to distinguish the various shades of timbre of a violin; richness, distinctness, and consonance of timbre are brought out on the spectrograms.

The analysis of the recordings of transient factors is also full of difficulties. It is well known that the transients are a considerable factor in our estimate of the quality of an instrument, and general laws have been deduced on this point. Nevertheless, systematic studies remain to be done.

In spite of all these difficulties, the objective study of the quality of an instrument offers enormous advantages over the old sonority contests. It is now possible to make out a chart of the characteristics giving an acoustical *portrait* of an instrument. I have done this for the violin; the correlation between the subjective appreciations and the results obtained by noting the parameters is satisfactory. One can then define whole series of instruments objectively and classify them in order of quality; their great number is no longer the difficulty it was in the old contests.

The table of an instrument's characteristics offers various points of interest: it can be used for survey purposes; the instrument's response curve can serve the same purpose as fingerprints; it offers a means of control during manufacture; it can give indications which will be useful in the making of new instruments. The methods applied here to the violin can be adapted to other instruments. The last illustration reproduces a table of characteristics which I have used, a table susceptible of improvement or completion (some instruments, for example, need to be studied for accuracy). This table of characteristics is the basis of all progress in instrument making. It represents a real acoustical portrait of the instrument. To make it and to interpret it obviously demand a considerable amount of knowledge: materials, construction, playing, techniques of recording and analysis, etc.

The violin is constructed with the help of crafts or semi-industrial techniques; the quality of the resulting products varies greatly, first of all because of the variations in the natural materials employed, for which reason the traditional empiricism has marked time since Stradivari. The mystery and sentimentalism with which many instrument makers surround themselves is out of date: it is now established that the quality of an industrial product is connected with the existence of a laboratory, that is to say, with scientific research; some industrial manufacturers of musical instruments are beginning to be aware of this. Much scientific work on the violin is being done in almost all parts of the world, and there is no doubt that the results obtained will pass sooner or later from the laboratory to the workshop or the factory.

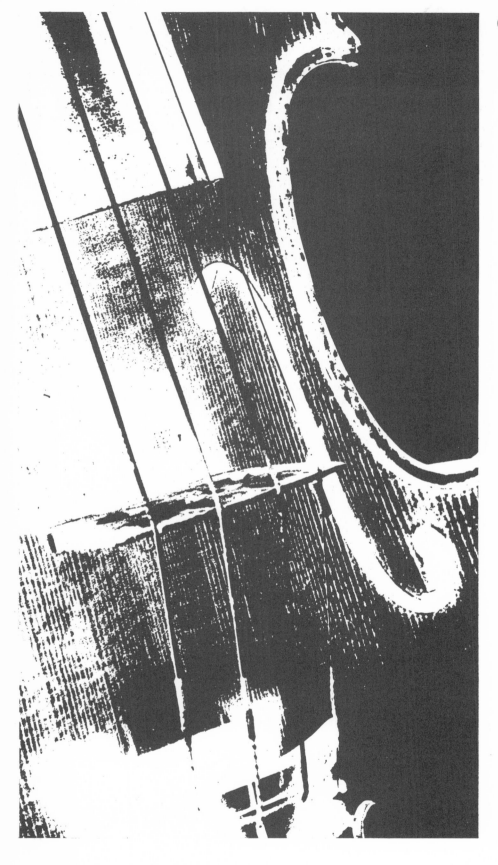

CONCLUSION

6

This book studies a musical instrument, a machine for producing sounds, which has been in use for four centuries; it strips it of the stories and legends with which it has been adorned. Elaborated by craftsmen and gradually brought to perfection, the violin is still often surrounded with a halo of mystery which the empirical basis of its manu-facture explains. It is an archetype of instrument making; it represents a whole family of instruments; it holds an all-important place in our music. In many countries it has replaced more primitive traditional instruments, thanks to its almost unlimited possi-bilities. Composers in the front rank are still drawing new effects from it. Because of its simplicity and perfection, it will be difficult to replace.

Some querulous minds consider the intrusion of science into instrument making as a kind of profanation. For them instrument making is a cult and Stradivari a god. But the secrets attributed to Stradivari cannot stand up to scientific investigation. Giovanni Iviglia, quoted by Vannes in the preface to the Dictionnaire des luthiers *(141), said in his time:*

Between the naive theories of the honest Giovanni Antonio Marchi, who dedicated an instrument to the Lord before he closed it, imploring Him to bestow sonority upon it, and the prosopopoeia of other makers who seemed to base their science upon more or less expressive winks of the eyelid, there must be something concrete, not supernatural, representing the experience of so many human lives, realist and positive, stripped of all charlatanism.

I hope to have contributed here towards demolishing many legends. There is no question of depreciating the merits of Stradivari, but of assigning him his proper place, and of offering some objective data in the field of instrument making.

A probable history of the violin has been sketched, based on elements which can be controlled: documents and technical arguments. Certain instruments have been dis-cussed which may be considered as ancestors of the violin. We have seen how all the documents turn our eyes towards Lyons where, between 1550 and 1570, Duiffoprugcar was the outstanding personality, capable of bringing about a sudden alteration in the family of rebecs.

Several attempts at perfecting the violin have been mentioned and their failures pointed out. Evolution is asymptotic; it becomes more and more difficult to perfect an instrument such as the violin. But it would be rash to assert that it has reached the end of its evolution. New musical demands and fresh techniques continue to arise. From summary experiments in the use of plastic materials, it has been too rapidly concluded that these are not suitable. It is certain that the shape and actual dimensions of the violin are good for the woods traditionally employed. If the material is changed, the shape must be changed, adapting one to the other, without abandoning the fundamental con-ception of the violin for all that. This presupposes methods of experimental instrument making, which Savart had the merit of attempting. To hope to perfect the violin and yet retain its simplicity is an illusion, but the fact remains that it is possible to adapt it to modern conditions and new materials.

We have seen that from the aesthetic point of view the shape of the violin is not arbitrary, but the result of the application of rules which were well known at the time the violin was first made. The methods of design linked with the golden number have nothing mysterious about them; they have simply been forgotten. The directive designs suggested herein are within the range of an ordinary craftsman, and they have reasonable aesthetic justification. They allow us to get beyond the stage of mere copying, and to do once more what the ancient instrument makers did with sufficient variations to avoid monotony. There has been a great deal of argument about the golden number; men have attributed to it virtues it never had, and have surrounded it with metaphysical considerations. Removed from this context, the golden number becomes a practical number, allowing the production of a rational shape with the minimum effort.

The section on technique has briefly explained how to construct a violin with the aid of engineering techniques, in the same way as we construct a bridge or an electric generator. I have pointed out that materials can be studied objectively; I have shown that the shape used by the instrument makers achieves an optimum resistance of the materials to deformation. The ovolo, the catenary, and the ellipse have been empirically known for centuries and can be mathematically justified. The violin achieves an effective superposition of aesthetic and functional designs. The problem of varnishing (about which countless foolish things have been said), like all the other problems, can be solved rationally. I have insisted on showing that the shape of the violin is practical from the point of view of durability. The whole instrument solves a complex problem of interactions combined into a homogeneous system. If we propose to modify one of the elements – for example, the material – we must reconsider the complete system, make an exhaustive study of it all over again. As well as being empirical (as it is still), the technique of instrument making can become precise.

The final section of this book, on acoustics, seems to me the most important. No coherent acoustical doctrine of musical instruments exists, and I have endeavoured to supply this need without becoming tedious over details which can only interest specialists. The originality, the interest, of a musical instrument lies primarily in its musical possibilities, in its audible product. Now, electro-acoustics have provided us in recent decades with devices which allow solutions to most of the violin's acoustical problems. We can now study, analyse, measure, and record every vibratory phenomenon and obtain a true photographic representation of it in colour and relief. Therefore it is possible to introduce the idea of measurement into instrument making and to replace the usual vague and subjective terminology by accurate units: decibels, Hertz, milliseconds, etc. I have pointed out a few peculiarities of the auditive mechanism, the role of which is important. We cannot study an emittor if we do not know the characteristics of the receiver destined to capture its signals. We cannot study the acoustics of musical instruments without having first defined the properties of the ear. Conversely, physiologists are mistaken in taking no interest in musical instruments which, like the violin, have been perfected gradually through contact with the ear, and which represent a reflection of the ear's properties.

The study of the emittor – of the instrument proper – comprises two distinct parts: excitation and amplification. We have seen that a string over which a bow is drawn vibrates in several ways, that these vibratory modes determine the form of the excitation signal, and that they are connected with physical parameters which, being very definite, can be measured and regulated at will. The phenomena are much more complex than the elementary theory of vibrating strings would indicate, but the acoustic signal of *excitation can be recorded and analysed without special difficulty. This signal is com-municated to the instrument proper, considered as the total of a series of elementary resonators coupled one to another, the properties of which are determined by the instru-ment's response curve. The response curve can be regulated at will by manipulating the different parts of the instrument; it is this curve that determines the quality of the instrument, because the signal radiated by it is the result of the superposition, or com-bination, of the form of the signal from the string with that of the response curve. I have stressed that the energy resulting from the contact between string and bow was communi-cated to the instrument not only by the bridge, but also by the contact points of the ends of the strings, the distribution of the initial energy being dependent on the structure of the instrument.*

Lastly, the signal radiated by the instrument and perceived by the listener is an objective phenomenon which can be recorded and analysed in its smallest details. The form of this signal conditions the acoustical quality of the instrument, and this quality can now be appreciated objectively. I have made this possibility concrete by establishing a table of the characteristics of the violin, which permits an objective judgment, based on documents, to be passed on the instrument. This table allows instruments to be compared and classified, thus making sonority contests more reasonable than they used to be.

This study does not put an end to research on the violin; the 'tools for thought' with which the great modern theories furnish us, the scientific methods and apparatus are evolving and becoming more perfect every day, and are continually bringing into question most of the problems that were once considered solved. The violin, whose effectiveness, simplicity, and perfection cannot be surpassed, still offers a rich field for investigation.

1 R. ALTON. *Violin and cello building and repairing*, London, Cassel, 1946.

2 S. ARAKELIAN. *Le violon*. Téhéran, Institut franco-iranien, 1952.

3 U. ARNS. *Untersuchungen an Geigen*, Karlsruhe, 1955. (Thesis at the *Technische Hochschule*, Karlsruhe.)

4 U. ARNS. *Eine neue Art objektiver Qualitätsfeststellung von Geigen*, in *Gravesaner Blätter*, Mayence, 7–8, 1957, p. 92.

5 H. BACKHAUS. *Über Resonanzeigenschaften von Streichinstrumenten*, in *Akutische Zeitschrift*, I/S, 1936, p. 179.

6 H. BACKAUS, *Über neuere Ergebnisse der Geigenforschung*, in *Akustische Zeitschrift*, 4, 1939, Heft 5, pp. 302–311.

7 A. BAGATELLA. *Regole per la costruzione de' violini, viole, violoncelli et violoni. Memoria presentata alla Accademia di scienze, lettere et arti di Padova*, 1782.

8 BARKECHLI. *Quelques idées nouvelles sur la consonance*, in *Acoustique musicale*, Paris, C.N.R.S., 1959. (Colloques intern. C.N.R.S., 84.)

9 J. BECQUEREL. *Coursde physique: élasticité, acoustique*, Paris, Hermann, 1926.

10 A. BECK. *Die proportionale Konstruktion der Geige*, Leipzig, 1923.

11 B. BLADIER. *Sur la vitesse de vibration des cordes filées sur boyau*, in *C.-r. Ac. sc.*, vol. CCXXXVIII, 1954, p. 570.

12 B. BLADIER. *Sur la caisse sonore, l'ame et le chevalet du violoncelle*, in *C.-r. Ac. sc.*, vol. CCXLC, 1957, p. 791.

13 B. BLADIER. *Nouvelle étude sur la vibration des cordes dans les instruments de musique*, in *J. phys. et le rad.*, vol. XV, 1954, p. 66.

14 B. BLADIER. *De l'influence de la vitesse et de la pression de l'archet sur la vitesse de vibration des cordes filées*, in *C.-r. Ac. sc.*, vol. CCXL, 1955, p. 1868.

15 B. BLADIER. *Nouvelles recherches concernant la vibration de cordes de violoncelle*, in *J. phys. et le rad.*, vol. XVI, 1955, p. 108.

16 B. BLADIER. *Évolution des phénomènes transitoires dans la mise en vibration des cordes*, in *J. phys. et le rad.*, vol. XVII, 1956, p. 57.

17 B. BLADIER. *Contribution a l'étude du violoncelle*, in *Acoustique musicale*, Paris, C.N.R.S., 1959. (Colloques intern. C.N.R.S., 84.)

18 PH. BONANNI, S.J. *Traité des vernis*, Paris, L. d'Houry, 1723.

19 H. BOUASSE. *Cordes et membranes*, Paris, Delagrave, 1926.

20 H. BOUASSE. *Verges et plaques. Cloches et carillons.* Paris, Delagrave, 1927.

21 H. BOUASSE. *Tuyaux et résonateurs*, Paris, Delagrave, 1929.

22 J. BRILLOUIN. *Réflexions sur les problèmes d'acoustique musicale*, in *Acoustique musicale*, Paris, C.N.R.S., 1959. (Colloques intern. C.N.R.S., 84.)

23 H. BRINER. *Notiz über die unterschiedliche Wirkung der Schall-Absorbtion auf den Klang von neuen und alten Geigen*. Experimentia, Birckhäuser, vol. VII, 2, 1951.

24 G. BRUHAT. *Physique générale. Mécanique*, Paris, Masson, 1955.

25 R. CABARAT. *Mesure des constantes élastiques des matériaux par un procédé acoustique*, in *C.-r. Ac. sc.*, vol. CCXIII, 1941, p. 231.

26 R. CABARAT. *Nouvelle méthode dynamique de mesure du module d'élasticité et de la capacité d'amortissement*, in *Verein deutsche Ing. Berichte*, vol. VIII, 1956, p. 156.

27 F. CABOS. *Le violon et la lutherie*, Paris, Gründ, 1948.

28 E. CHARRON. *Théorie de l'archet*, Paris, Gauthier-Villars, 1916. (Thesis.)

29 J. CHENANTAIS. *Le violoniste et le violon*, Nantes, Durance, 1927. (Contains an interesting account of sonority competitions between ancient and modern violins and cellos.)

30 H. COUTAGNE. *Gaspard Duiffoprugcar et les luthiers lyonnais*, Paris, Fischbacher, 1893.

31 G. DEMENY. *Physiologie des professions: le violoniste*, Paris, Maloine, 1905.

32 A. ENGEL. *Descriptive catalogue of the musical instruments in the South Kensington Museum*, London, 1874.

33 F.-J. FÉTIS. *Antoine Stradivari, luthier célèbre connu sous le nom de Stradivarius, précédé de recherches historiques et critiques sur l'origine et les transformations des instruments à archet*, Paris, Vuillaume, 1856.

34 E. FINE. *Dynamic methods for determining the elastic constants and their temperature variation in metals*, in *Am. soc. for testing materials*, New York, 1952.

35 G. FRY. *Italian varnishes*, London, Stevens and sons, 1904.

36 C. FUHR. *Die akustischen Rätsel der Geige*, Frankfurt am Main, Hofmeister, 1958.

37 M.-C. GHYKA. *Essai sur le rythme*, Paris, Gallimard, 1938.

38 P. GREENE. *Violin performance with the reference to tempered, natural and pythagorean intonation*, in *Univ. Iowa Studies in psych. of music*, vol. IV, 1937, p. 232.

39 J. GALLAY. *Les luthiers italiens aux XVIIe et XVIIIe siècles*, Paris, Acad. des bibliophiles, 1869. (New edition of *La chèlonomie ou le parfait luthier*, by A. Sibire, 1806.)

40 L. GREILSAMER. *Le vernis de Crémone*, Paris, Soc. fr. d'impr., 108.

41 L. GREILSAMER. *L'hygiène du violon*, Paris, Delagrave, 1910.

42 L. GREILSAMER. *Anatomie et physiologie du violon*, Paris, Delagrave, 1924.

43 L. GRILLET. *Les ancêtres du violon et du violoncelle; les luthiers et les fabricants d'archets*, Paris, Schmid, 1901.

44 M. GRUETZMACHER. *Das Teiltonspektrum einer Glocke*, in *Gravesaner Blätter*, no. XIII, 1959, p. 124.

45 M. GRUETZMACHER. *Le spectre d'un son de cloche*, in *Acoustique musicale*, Paris, C.N.R.S., 1959, p. 239. (Colloques intern. C.N.R.S., 84.)

46 F. HAMMA. *Meisterwerke italienischer Geigenbaukunst*, Stuttgart, Hamma, 1932.

47 F. HAMMA. *Meisterwerke deutscher Geigenbaukunst*, Stuttgart, Hamma, 1948.

48 G. HART. *Le violon, les luthiers célèbres et leurs imitateurs*, Paris, Schott, fr., 1886.

49 HERRADE DE LANDSBERG. *Hortus deliciarum*, Strasbourg, Oberlin, 1945.

50 W. E. HILL. *Antonio Stradivarius*, London, Hill, 1908.

51 W. E. HILL. *Gio. Paolo Maggini*, London, Hill, 1892.

52 E.-C.-A. JACQUOT. *La lutherie lorraine et française depuis ses origines jusqu'a nos jours, d'après les archives locales*, Paris, Fischbacher, 1912.

53 P. KAUL. *La querelle des anciens et des modernes*, Nantes, Kaul, 1927.

54 F. KELLER. *Beitrag zur Nachbildung des menschlichen Gehörs im Rahmen raumakustischer Modellversuche*, in *Gravesaner Blätter*, no. X, 1958, p. 72.

55 E. W. KUENZI. *Methods for determining the elastic constants of non metallic materials*, in *Am. soc. for testing materials*, New York, 1952.

56 L. DE LA LAURENCE. *L'école française de violon, de Lully à Viotti*, Paris, Delagrave, 1922–24, 3 vol.

57 CH. LALO. *Éléments d'esthétique*, Paris, Vuibert, 1925.

58 E. LEIPP. *Aspects du problème des gammes instrumentales*, in *Musique et radio*, Paris, October, 1958.

59 E. LEIPP. *Le module d'élasticité et la masse spécifique: paramètres sensibles du spectre d'une corde harmonique*, in *C.-r. Ac. sc.*, vol. CCXLVIII, 1959, p. 3278.

60 E. LEIPP. *Le module de rigidité et la tension par unité de surface de la section: paramètres sensibles du rendement musical d'une corde harmonique*, in *C.-r. Ac. sc.*, vol. CCXLIX, 1959, p. 375.

61 E. LEIPP. *La vibration d'octave, paramètre sensible dans les spectres des instruments à cordes*, in *C.-r. Ac. sc.*, vol. CCXLIX, 1959, p. 1474.

62 E. LEIPP. *Le degré hygrométrique de l'air ambiant, paramètre sensible du spectre d'une corde harmonique de boyau*, in *C.-r. Ac. sc.*, vol. CCXLIX, 1959, p. 2014.

63 E. LEIPP. *Essai sur la lutherie*, Paris, Millant, 1945.

64 E. LEIPP. *La sonorité du violon, de l'alto, du violoncelle*, Paris, Millant, 1952.

65 E. LEIPP. *Étude sur les origines du violon*, in *Musique et radio*, Paris, April–July, 1953.

66 E. LEIPP. *Le violon et le nombre d'or*, in *Musique et radio*, Paris, October, 1954.

67 E. LEIPP. *L'homogénéité de niveau du violon*, in *Musique et radio*, Paris, January, 1956.

68 E. LEIPP. *Aspects physiques du problème du vernissage des instruments*, in *Musique et radio*, Paris, March 1959.

69 E. LEIPP. *Le violon de Savart*, in *Musique et radio*, Paris, June 1959.

70 E. LEIPP. *La synthèse du spectre des cordes harmoniques*, in *Das Musikinstrument*, Frankfurt, April 1960.

71 E. LEIPP. *Akustik and Musikinstrumente*, in *Gravesanar Blätter*, no. XXII, 1961, p. III.

72 E. LEIPP. *Le problème du diapason*, in *Das Musikinstrument*, Frankfurt, 1961.

73 E. LEIPP and A. MOLES. *L'emploi du sonagraphe dans la détermination de la qualité des instruments a cordes*; communication présentée au Group. ac. de langue francaise, Lausanne, September 1958, in *Annales des télécommunications*, vol. XIV, no. 5–6, 1959, p. 135.

74 E. LEIPP and A. MOLES. *Méthode objective d'appréciation des qualités d'un instrument a cordes*, Amsterdam, Elsevier, 1961. (Communication to the International acoustical congress, Stuttgart, 1959.)

75 E. LEIPP and A. MOLES. *Aktuelle Probleme des experimentellen Geigenbaues*, in *Gravesaner Blätter*, no. XIX–XX, 1960.

76 F. LESURE. *Notes sur la facture du violon au XVIe siècle*, in *Revue musicale*, no. 226, Paris, 1955.

77 J. C. R. LICKLIDER. *Auditory frequency analysis*, in *Information theory*, London, 1956.

78 M. W. LOTTERMOSER. *Orgelneubau auf akustischer Grundlage*, in *Gravesaner Blätter*, no. XI–XII, 1958, p. 131.

79 M. W. LOTTERMOSER. *L'examen acoustique des violons dans la* Physikalische-Technische Bundesanstalt, in *Acoustique musicale*, Paris, C.N.R.S., 1959, p. 185. (Colloques intern. C.N.R.S., 84.)

80 LUTGENDORF. *Die Geigen und Lautenmacher vom Mittelalter bis zur Gegenwart*, Frankfurt am Main, 1922.

81 V.-C. MAHILLON. *Éléments d'acoustique musicale et instrumentale*, Bruxelles, Mahillon, 1874.

82 E. MAILAND. *Découverte des anciens vernis italiens employés pour les instruments a cordes et à archets*, Paris, Lacroix et Baudry, 1859.

83 E. MAILLARD. *Du nombre d'or*, Paris, Éd. de Tournon, 1943.

84 CH. MAILLOT. *La fabrication des cordes harmoniques. Manuel du luthier*, Paris, Larousse, 1952.

85 J.-C. MAUGIN and W. MAIGNE. *Nouveau manuel complet du luthier*, new ed., Paris, Roret, 1894.

86 H. MEINEL. *Frequenzkurven von Geigen,* in *Akustik Zeitschrift,* 2, 1937, p. 185.

87 H. MEINEL. *Akustische Eigenschaften von Geigen verschiedener Qualität,* in *Akustik Zeitschrift,* 4, 1939, p. 89.

88 H. MEINEL. *Zur schalltechnischen Prüfung der klanglichen Qualität von Geigen,* in *Zeitsch. für technische Physik,* 10, 1938, p. 297.

89 H. MEINEL. *Regarding the sound quality of violins and a scientific basis for violin construction,* in *Journ. ac. soc. Am.,* vol. XXIX, 1957, p. 817.

90 FR. M. MERSENNE. *Harmonie universelle,* French ed., Paris, S. Cramoisy, 1636–1637.

91 E. MEYER and BUCHMANN. *Die Klang-spektren der Musikinstrumente,* Berlin, 1931

92 W. MEYER-EPPLER, H. SENDHOFF, and R. RUPPRATH. *Residualton und Formantton,* in *Gravesaner Blätter,* no. XIV, 1959, p. 70.

93 R. and M. MILLANT. *Manuel pratique du luthier,* Paris, Larousse, 1952.

94 A. MOLES. *Pourquoi deux violons font-ils plus de bruit qu'un seul?* in *Journ. phys. et le rad.,* vol. X, no. VIII, 1949, p. 194.

95 A. MOLES. *Étude et représentation de la note complexe en acoustique musicale,* in *Annales des télécommunications,* vol. VII, no. 2, 1952, p. 430.

96 A. MOLES. *Structure physique du signal musical et phonétique,* 1952. (Thesis at the Sorbonne.)

97 A. MOLES. *L'emploi du spectrographe acoustique et le problème de la partition en musique expérimentale,* in *Annales des télécommunications,* vol. XII, no. 9, 1957, p. 299.

98 A. MOLES. *Physique et technique du bruit,* Paris, Dunod, 1952.

99 A. MOLES. *Les musiques expérimentales,* Paris, Éd. Cercle d'art contemporain, 1960.

100 L. MORDRET. *La lutherie artistique,* Paris, Quantin, 1885.

101 R. MUNOZ. *Technologia de la guitarra argentina,* Buenos Aires, 1952. (Contains an interesting study of South American woods.)

102 H. F. OLSON. *Musical engineering,* New York, 1952.

103 G. PASQUALINI. *L'étude électro-acoustique de la caisse harmonique.* (International congress on electro-acoustics, Delft, 1953.)

104 G. PASQUALINI. *Nuovi resultai nello studio della cassa armonica,* in *Ricerca scient.,* 1943, p. 111.

105 G. PASQUALINI. *Relazione sulle prove per addivenire ad una valutazione obbietiva della qualita acustiche di alcuni violini,* in *Ricerca scient.,* vol. XVIII, 1940, p. 622.

106 G. PASQUALINI and I. BARDUCCI. *Misura dell'attrito interno et delle costanti elastiche del legno,* in *Nuovo Cimento,* vol. V, no. 5, 1948, p. 416.

107 E. PELUZZI. *Antonio Stradivari ha parlato,* Milan, Bocca, 1941.

108 L. PIMONOV. *Contribution a l'étude de problèmes de la sélectivité tonale de l'oreille,* in *Rev. de laryngologie,* nos. 1–2, 1959, p. 78.

109 L. PIMONOV. *La détermination de la qualité des instruments de musique au moyen du spectre sonore transitoire,* in *Acoustique musicale,* Paris, C.N.R.S., 1959. (Colloques intern. C.N.R.S., 84.)

110 M. PINCHERLE. *Les instruments du quatuor,* Paris, P.U.F., 1948.

111 R. K. POTTER and G. E. PETERSON. *The representations of vowels and their movements,* in *Journ. ac. soc. Am.,* vol. II, 528, 1948.

112 M. PRAETORIUS. *Syntagma musicum* (vol. II, *De organographia*), Wolfenbüttel, 1618 (reissued Berlin, Trautwein, 1884).

113 C. V. RAMAN. *Handbuch der Physik,* Berlin, Springer, 1927, vol. VIII.

114 J. T. RICHARDS. *An evaluation of several static and dynamic methods for determining elastic moduli,* in *Am. soc. for testing materials,* New York, 1952, p. 71.

115 A. V. RIMSKI-KORSAKOV. *Les recherches sur le timbre des violons et guitares et sur l'excitation des vibrations d'une anche d'harmonium*, in *Acoustique musicale*, Paris, C.N.R.S., 1959, p. 203. (Colloques intern. C.N.R.S., 84.)

116 H. RITTER. *Die Viola alta oder Altgeige*, Leipzig, Merseburger, 1885.

117 E. ROHLOFF. *Über die innere Reibung und Strahlungsdämpfung bei Geigen*, in *Ann. der Phys.*, vol. XXXVIII, 1940, p. 177.

118 A. ROUSSEL. *Traité de lutherie*, Paris, Durand, 1956.

119 J. RUHLMANN. *Die Geschichte der Bogeninstrumente*, Braunschweig, Vieweg, 1882.

120 F. A. SAUNDERS. *The mechanical action of violins*, in *Jour. ac. soc. Am.*, vol. IX, 1937, p. 81.

121 F. A. SAUNDERS. *Recent work on violins*, in *Journ. ac. soc. Am.*, vol. XXV, 3, 1953.

122 F. A. SAUNDERS. *A scientific search for the secret of Stradivarius*, in *Journal of the Franklin Inst.*, vol. 229/1, 1940.

123 F. SAVART. *Mémoire sur la construction des instruments a cordes et à archet.* (Followed by the report made to the two Academies of Sciences and of Arts by J.-B. Biot), Paris, Déterville, 1819.

124 P. SCHAEFFER and A. MOLES. *A la recherche d'une musique concrète*, Paris, Éd. du Seuil, 1952.

125 J. F. SCHOUTEN. *Residuentheorie*, in *Philipps technische Rundschau*, vol. V, 1940, p. 294.

126 J. F. SCHOUTEN. *Zur Tonhöhenempfindung* (in collaboration with B. LOPEZ CARDOZO), Amsterdam, Elzevier, 1961. (Communication 3 N 6, International acoustical congress, Stuttgart, 1959.)

127 K. SCHUEGERL. *Die Rolle des Gehörsorgans im Aufbau der Musik*, in *Gravesaner Blätter*, no. XIII, 1959, p. 2.

128 C. SCHULZE. *Stradivaris Geheimnis*, Berlin, Füssinger, 1901.

129 C. SEASHORE. *Psychology of music*, New York, McGraw-Hill, 1938.

130 N. SIMOUTRE. *Aux amateurs du violon*, Paris, 1900.

131 E. SKUDRZYK. *Die Bedeutung der Ausgleichvorgänge für die Musik und Tonübertragung*, in *Elektrotech. und Maschinenbau*, 67 (9 and 10), 1950.

132 E. SKUDRZYK. *Betrachtungen zum musikalischen Zusammenklang*, in *Congrès intern. d'électro-acoustique*, Delft, 1953, p. 249.

133 E. SKUDRZYK. *Psychoakustische Erscheinungen bei der Bildung von natürliche und synthetischen Klängen*, in *Gravesaner Blätter*, no. IX, 1957, p. 75.

134 K. STEINER. *Die geometrische Konstruktion der Geigenform von Stradivari*, in *Instrumentenbau Zeitschr.*, 9, 1949.

135 STEVENS and DAVIS. *Hearing*. London, Wiley, 1938.

136 P.-F. TINGRY. *Traité théorique et pratique sur l'art de faire et d'appliquer les vernis*, Genève, Manget, 1803.

137 A. TOLBECQUE. *L'art du luthier*, Niort, Mercier, 1903.

138 F. TRAUTWEIN. *Probleme des Hörens*, in *Gravesaner Blätter*, no. VII-VIII, 1957.

139 A. TRIPIER and M. DEVAUX. *Traité théorique et pratique sur l'art de faire le vernis*, Paris, Mathias, 1845.

140 VAN ESBROEK and MONTFORT. *Qu'est-ce que jouer juste?*, Bruxelles, Lumiére, 1948.

141 R. VANNES. *Essai d'un dictionnaire universel des luthiers*, Bruxelles, les amis de la musique, 1951. (Gives an interesting survey of the role of ancient violins and their imitation.)

142 S. VIRDUNG. *Musica getutscht...* S. l. n. d. (Bâle, 1511).

143 J.-F. WATIN. *L'art du peintre doreur et vernisseur*, Paris, Durand, 1773.

144 F. WINCKEL. *Klangwelt unter der Lupe*, Berlin, M. Hesse, 1952.

145 F. WINCKEL. *Die Kunst des Geigenbaues*, Berlin, Voigt, 1954.

146 F. WINCKEL, *Die Bedeutung des Vibrato in der Musik*, in *Gravesaner Blätter*, no. VI, 1957, p. 40.

147 F. WINCKEL. *Das Ohr als Zeitmessorgan*, in *Gravesaner Blätter*, no. IX, 1957, p. 83.

148 F. WINCKEL. *Influence des facteurs psycho-physiologiques sur la sensation de consonance-dissonance*, in *Acoustique musicale*, Paris, C.N.R.S., 1959. (Colloques intern. C.N.R.S., 84.)

149 F. WINCKEL. *Die subjektive Bewertung des Residuums*, Amsterdam, Elzevier, 1961. (Communication to the International acoustical congress, Stuttgart, 1959.)

150 F. WINCKEL. *Stilkriterien der neuen Musik*, Berlin, Merseburger, 1961.

151 R. W. YOUNG. *Inharmonicity of plain wire piano strings*, in *Journ. ac. soc. Am.*, 24/3, 1952, p. 267.

152 R. W. YOUNG. *The tuning of musical instruments*, Elkhart (Indiana), Inst. of music. instr. technology. 1953.

153 R. W. YOUNG. *Influence of humidity on the tuning of a piano*, in *Journ. ac. soc. Am.*, 21/6, 1949, p. 580.

154 R. W. YOUNG. *Sur l'intonation de divers instruments de musique du U.S. Navy Electronics Laboratory, San Diego*, in *Acoustique musicale*, Paris, C.N.R.S., 1959. (Colloques intern., C.N.R.S., 84.)

155 R. W. YOUNG and J. C. WEBSTER. *Die Innenstimmung von Musikinstrumenten*, in *Gravesaner Blätter*, no. XI–XII, 1958, p. 175.

156 A. ZILOTY. *La découverte de Jean Van Eyck*, Paris, Floury, 1941.

This book
was designed by
PETER DORN
and was printed by
University of
Toronto
Press